THEORY OF EQUATIONS

THEORY
OF EQUATIONS

BY

JOSEPH MILLER THOMAS
Professor of Mathematics
Duke University

FIRST EDITION

McGRAW-HILL BOOK COMPANY, Inc.
NEW YORK AND LONDON
1938

THE MAPLE PRESS COMPANY, YORK, PA.

PREFACE

This book is intended to serve as a text for a term's course open to graduate and advanced undergraduate students. The material included is slightly more than the author has been accustomed to cover with his classes in the subject.

In writing the book, the author has been guided by a two-fold purpose: to make the treatment agree in spirit and terminology with what is called modern algebra, and to lead up to the Galois theory, which he may include with topics more advanced or more specialized in a second volume.

The form of statement and the proof of some of the results are thought to be new, at least in a book of this character. The following may be cited in illustration of this point: the classification of permutations into even and odd without the use of an alternating function; the discussion of linear systems; the statement of Budan's and Sturm's theorems so as to include the upper end point of the segment considered; the proof of Budan's theorem; the elementary discussion of a limit to the error in Horner's method; the discussion of the resultant; and finally the solution of simultaneous non-linear systems, a topic usually avoided in texts on the theory of equations. It is hoped that the sum total of these features, together with the choice and arrangement of subject matter, justifies the publication of a textbook in so old a branch, for the teaching of which two such excellent books as Dickson's are already available.

Valuable suggestions have been received from students over a period of years. More recently, Messrs. Grady Frank,

W. G. McGavock, and L. I. Wade have read the manuscript in whole or in part and have materially improved it by their criticisms. The last two of these and Dr. R. W. Stokes and Mr. W. L. Morris have helped in the proofreading. From time to time many valuable suggestions have been received from Professor Leonard Carlitz. Dr. Alta Odoms not only prepared the manuscript for publication, but also read both galley and page proof in most painstaking fashion. Professor R. C. Archibald kindly placed at the author's disposal some of the material in the well-stocked library of Brown University. To all these the author is very grateful.

J. M. Thomas.

Durham, N. C.,
June, 1938.

CONTENTS

PAGE

PREFACE v

CHAPTER I
INTRODUCTION

SECTION
1. THE NUMBER SYSTEM. 1
2. FACTORIZATION. 4
3. EUCLID'S DIVISION ALGORITHM. 5
4. UNIQUE FACTORIZATION. 10
5. CONGRUENCES 11
6. RESIDUES 12

CHAPTER II
PERMUTATIONS

7. DEFINITIONS AND NOTATION. 15
8. PRODUCTS OF PERMUTATIONS. 17
9. MULTIPLICATION NOT COMMUTATIVE 18
10. POWERS. 19
11. FACTORIZATION INTO TRANSPOSITIONS. 22
12. EVEN AND ODD PERMUTATIONS. 22
13. SYMMETRIC AND ALTERNATING GROUPS 23

CHAPTER III
DETERMINANTS

14. DEFINITION 25
15. ELEMENTARY TRANSFORMATIONS 27
16. ALGEBRAIC COMPLEMENT 29
17. MINORS. 29
18. THE SUMMATION CONVENTION 30
19. THE DELTAS AND EPSILONS 31
20. EXPANSION OF A DETERMINANT. 32
21. COMPLETION OF THE PROOFS FOR THE ELEMENTARY TRANSFOR-
MATIONS 33

SECTION   PAGE
22. EVALUATION OF DETERMINANTS   34
23. BORDERED DETERMINANTS.   37
24. MATRICES.   38

CHAPTER IV
SYSTEMS OF LINEAR EQUATIONS

25. n LINEAR EQUATIONS IN n UNKNOWNS.   41
26. EXCEPTIONAL CASES   43
27. HOMOGENEOUS SYSTEMS.   44
28. NON-HOMOGENEOUS LINEAR SYSTEMS   49

CHAPTER V
POLYNOMIALS IN A SINGLE INDETERMINATE

29. DEFINITIONS.   54
30. DIVISION OF POLYNOMIALS.   55
31. SYNTHETIC DIVISION   56
32. THE REMAINDER AND FACTOR THEOREMS   58
33. DERIVATIVES.   59
34. MULTIPLE ROOTS.   61
35. HIGHEST COMMON FACTOR OF TWO POLYNOMIALS.   61
36. ELIMINATION OF MULTIPLE ROOTS   63
37. REDUCIBILITY   63
38. GAUSS' LEMMA.   64
39. REDUCIBILITY IN THE RATIONAL FIELD   65
40. EISENSTEIN'S THEOREM.   67

CHAPTER VI
GRAPHICAL METHODS

41. COORDINATE SYSTEMS.   69
42. THE GRAPH OF AN EQUATION.   70
43. GRAPHICAL REPRESENTATION OF COMPLEX NUMBERS   72
44. DE MOIVRE'S THEOREM.   76
45. POLYNOMIALS FOR SMALL VALUES OF THE INDETERMINATE. . .   77
46. CONSEQUENCES OF THE TAYLOR DEVELOPMENT.   79
47. POLYNOMIALS FOR LARGE VALUES OF THE INDETERMINATE. . .   82

CHAPTER VII
ROOTS OF UNITY

48. UNITY HAS n nTH ROOTS   83
49. THE CUBE ROOTS OF UNITY   84

SECTION   PAGE

50. PERIOD OF ROOTS. 85
51. MULTIPLICATION OF ROOTS 86
52. PRIMITIVE ROOTS. 86
53. ALL THE nTH ROOTS EXPRESSED IN TERMS OF A PRIMITIVE ROOT 87
54. NUMBER OF PRIMITIVE ROOTS 87
55. GRAPHICAL REPRESENTATION. 88
56. THE EQUATION SATISFIED BY ALL THE PRIMITIVE nTH ROOTS . 89
57. IRREDUCIBILITY OF THE CYCLOTOMIC EQUATION. 90
58. BINOMIAL EQUATIONS. 91
59. AN IRREDUCIBLE BINOMIAL EQUATION. 92

CHAPTER VIII
SINGLE EQUATION IN SINGLE UNKNOWN

60. THE FUNDAMENTAL THEOREM OF ALGEBRA. 93
61. RELATIONS BETWEEN THE ROOTS AND THE COEFFICIENTS . . . 94
62. RATIONAL ROOTS. 96
63. IMAGINARY ROOTS 98
64. QUADRATIC SURD ROOTS. 99
65. TRANSFORMATION OF EQUATIONS 101
66. SOLUTION OF THE QUADRATIC. 103
67. SOLUTION OF THE CUBIC. 105
68. CUBICS WITH REAL COEFFICIENTS. 107
69. IRREDUCIBLE CASE OF THE CUBIC TREATED BY TRIGONOMETRY. 109
70. ALGEBRAIC DISCUSSION OF THE IRREDUCIBLE CASE 112
71. SOLUTION OF THE QUARTIC. 114
72. EQUATIONS OF HIGHER DEGREE 117
73. LOCATION OF ROOTS. 118
74. RELATIONS BETWEEN THE NUMBER OF REAL ROOTS OF A POLY-
    NOMIAL AND ITS DERIVATIVES 121
75. DESCARTES' RULE OF SIGNS 125
76. STURM'S POLYNOMIALS AND METHOD 127
77. APPROXIMATION BY A LINEAR EQUATION. 130
78. HORNER'S METHOD. 132

CHAPTER IX
SYMMETRIC FUNCTIONS

79. POLYNOMIALS IN SEVERAL INDETERMINATES 139
80. CONJUGATES. 141
81. Σ-POLYNOMIALS. 142
82. WEIGHT AND INDEX. 143

SECTION   PAGE
83. THE FUNDAMENTAL THEOREMS. 145
84. RELATION OF DEGREE AND NUMBER OF INDETERMINATES . . . 149
85. SUMS OF POWERS OF THE ROOTS 149
86. SYMMETRIC RATIONAL FUNCTIONS. 152

CHAPTER X
CONSTRUCTIBILITY

87. RULER AND COMPASS CONSTRUCTIONS. 154
88. CONSTRUCTIBLE NUMBERS 157
89. DUPLICATION OF THE CUBE 164
90. TRISECTION OF THE ANGLE. 164
91. THE REGULAR POLYGON OF n SIDES. 165

CHAPTER XI
RESULTANTS AND DISCRIMINANTS

92. THE CONDITION THAT TWO POLYNOMIALS HAVE A ROOT IN
    COMMON 169
93. SYLVESTER'S DIALYTIC ELIMINATION FOR A SPECIAL CASE . . . 171
94. THE GENERAL CASE 175
95. DISCRIMINANTS. 178
96. ALTERNATING POLYNOMIALS 182

CHAPTER XII
SIMULTANEOUS SYSTEMS

97. INEQUATIONS. 183
98. ALGEBRAIC SYSTEMS. 183
99. LOCATION AND COMPUTATION OF IMAGINARY ROOTS. 188

MISCELLANEOUS EXERCISES 191

BIBLIOGRAPHY. 197

INDEX 199

ANSWERS 205

THEORY OF EQUATIONS

CHAPTER I

INTRODUCTION

1. The Number System.—At the basis of elementary algebra are the positive integers 1, 2, 3, $\cdots$, which are introduced originally to count discrete objects. From them is developed the entire number system of analysis. With this the reader is supposed to be familiar, but its essential features will now be recalled. At the same time the convenient terms *ring* and *field* will be introduced.

The first number to be considered after the positive integers is zero (0), which is uniquely determined as the solution x of the equation $x + 1 = 1$.

If a is a positive integer, the negative integer $-a$ is uniquely determined as the solution x of $x + a = 0$.

The positive integers, the negative integers, and zero, which we shall denote collectively by $\mathcal{I}$, constitute the set of integers. The sum, difference, and product of two integers are integers. The set $\mathcal{I}$ is therefore said to be *closed* under the three operations denoted by $+$, $-$, $\times$.

If a, b, c are any three integers, they satisfy the following laws of combination:

(i) The associative law of addition:

(1.1)
$$a + (b + c) = (a + b) + c.$$

(ii) The associative law of multiplication:

(1.2)
$$a(bc) = (ab)c.$$

1

(iii) The commutative law of addition:

(1.3) $$a + b = b + a.$$

(iv) The commutative law of multiplication:

(1.4) $$ab = ba.$$

(v) The distributive law:

(1.5) $$a(b + c) = ab + ac.$$

Any set which satisfies the above laws and is closed under the operations $+$, $-$, $\times$ is called a (commutative) *ring*. The integers accordingly form a ring.

If a and b are integers and a is not zero, the rational number b/a is uniquely determined as the solution of $ax - b = 0$. Division by zero is not defined. Not only are the sum, difference, and product of two rational numbers rational, but the quotient of two rational numbers, whenever defined, is rational. The set of all rational numbers will be denoted by $\mathfrak{R}$. It is called the rational *field* because it has the characteristic properties defining a (commutative) field, namely, it is closed under the four rational operations $+$, $-$, $\times$, $\div$ and it satisfies (i) to (v).

The ring of integers $\mathfrak{g}$ is included in the field of rational numbers $\mathfrak{R}$ as a subset.

It is important to note that *a rational number can be defined as the quotient of two integers.* If the rational number is itself an integer, the denominator can be taken as 1.

The real numbers form a field $\mathfrak{X}$ which contains the integers, the rational numbers, and also the *irrational* numbers. The last mentioned can be approximated as closely as desired by rational numbers. Some of them are introduced in order to solve equations like $x^2 - 2 = 0$, which can be shown to have no rational solution. Their introduction is most readily accomplished by assuming the following

AXIOM OF CONTINUITY.—*If the real numbers are separated into two classes L, R such that*
   (i) *each class has at least one member;*
   (ii) *every real number is in one and only one class;*
   (iii) *every number in L is less than every number in R;*
then there is a greatest number in L or a least number in R, but not both.

Finally, there is the still more inclusive field 𝔷 of complex numbers, consisting of all numbers of the form $a + bi$, where a, b are real and i is a fixed root of the equation $x^2 + 1 = 0$.

The complex number $a + bi$ is (i) real if $b = 0$; (ii) imaginary if $b \neq 0$; and (iii) pure imaginary if $a = 0$, $b \neq 0$.

The following diagram, which exhibits the relation of the various sets to each other, merits careful study.

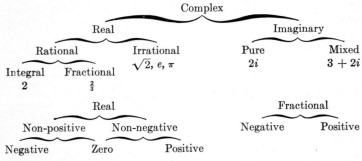

The reader should think of the complex number $a + bi$ as a formal symbol, which is algebraically combined with other like symbols just as if i were the literal representation of a real quantity. If a set of complex numbers is combined by rational operations in this manner and if the relation $i^2 = -1$ is used to lower the exponent of i in every term to 0 or to 1, the result can be expressed in the form $a + bi$, which is called by definition the complex answer to the computations. Considerable difficulty will be avoided if the reader realizes that the concept of complex number is purely formal. In short, all our statements about complex numbers amount to this and nothing more: if we make certain marks $(a + bi)$ on the blackboard or on paper and follow certain rules $[(1.1) - (1.5)$ above, and $i^2 = -1]$, certain other marks result.

The rational numbers and the integers have a table like that given above for real numbers, and the irrationals like that for fractions.

EXERCISES

1.1. There are sixteen different sets indicated in the diagram. Write their names in a vertical column. Head columns to the right with the signs $+$, $-$, $\times$, $\div$. Write "yes" or "no" in the columns to indicate under what operations each set is closed. Which sets are rings and which fields?

1.2. Assuming that the real numbers form a field, prove that the complex numbers also form a field.

1.3. Prove that the totality of numbers $a + b\sqrt{2}$, where a and b are rational, forms a field.

1.4. Prove that the totality of numbers $a + bi$, where a and b are integers, forms a ring.

2. Factorization.—If a and b are integers and if $b \neq 0$, the quotient a/b is a rational number. Hence a always is divisible by $b \neq 0$ in the rational field. The question of divisibility therefore does not arise in the rational field.

On the other hand, a/b may or may not be an integer. It will always be understood when we speak of divisibility of numbers that the set involved is the ring of integers.

The numbers ± 1 are divisors of every integer. For this reason they are called *units*.

Any integer a has the divisors ± 1, $\pm a$. If it has others, it is called *composite*. If it has no others and is not ± 1, it is called *prime*. Thus 3, 5, 7 are prime. *A prime is an integer other than ± 1 which has no factors except itself, its negative, and the units.* Since $0 = 3 \cdot 0$, zero is not a prime.

An integer is *even* or *odd* according as it is divisible by 2 or not. ± 2 are the only even primes.

It can be shown that the number of primes is infinite. To do so, suppose the contrary. There is then a greatest positive prime p. Let P be the product of all the positive primes. Since $P + 1 > p$, it cannot be a prime. On the other hand, it could only be divisible by a prime if 1 were so divisible. Hence we have a contradiction.

Every two integers a, b have the factors ± 1 in common. If they have no others, they are called *relatively prime*.[1] In particular, 1 and p are relatively prime, if p is any integer. Similarly, 15 and 16 are relatively prime.

3. Euclid's Division Algorithm.—Whether or not r_1 is divisible by r_2 ($\neq 0$), we can always apply the process of arithmetic to divide r_1 by r_2 until a non-negative remainder r_3 less than the absolute value of the divisor is found. This will be illustrated by numerical examples.

$$11 \mid 192 \mid 17$$
$$\underline{11}$$
$$82$$
$$\underline{77}$$
$$5$$

$$\frac{192}{11} = 17 + \frac{5}{11}$$
$$192 = 17 \cdot 11 + 5$$

The corresponding result for $192/(-11)$ is

$$192 = (-17)(-11) + 5,$$

obtained by introducing two minus signs in the first term.

If the dividend is minus, we must multiply by -1 and transform:

$$-192 = (17)(-11) - 5, \qquad -192 = (-17)(11) - 5.$$

---

[1] We shall often express this relationship by saying that "*a* is prime to *b*."

If we add to these $0 = (1)(-11) + 11$, $0 = (-1)(11) + 11$, we get

$$-192 = (18)(-11) + 6, \qquad -192 = (-18)(11) + 6.$$

In the general case, we have for the quotient q_1 of r_1/r_2

$$r_1 = q_1 r_2 + r_3,$$

with r_3 non-negative and less than $|r_2|$.[1]

If $r_3 \neq 0$, we may repeat on r_2/r_3,

$$r_2 = q_2 r_3 + r_4,$$

with r_4 less than r_3 and non-negative.   Thus we find a sequence of numbers

(3.1) $r_1, \quad r_2, \quad r_3, \quad r_4, \quad \cdots ,$

which satisfy

(3.2) $r_k = q_k r_{k+1} + r_{k+2}.$

Since r_k for $k > 2$ is decreasing and non-negative, the sequence must terminate, and since the process can be continued so long as the divisor is not zero, the last term must be zero.   From (3.2) we see (i) if an integer divides both r_k and r_{k+1}, it divides r_{k+2}, that is, if an integer is a divisor of two consecutive terms of (3.1), it is a divisor of their follower; (ii) if an integer is a divisor of both r_{k+1} and r_{k+2}, it is a divisor of r_k, that is, any integer which is a divisor of two consecutive terms of (3.1) is a divisor of their predecessor.   Hence any factor common to two consecutive members of (3.1) is a divisor of every member of the sequence.   In particular, if the last two terms are r_l, 0, then r_l is a divisor of the last two terms and hence of the first two.   Moreover, every integer which is a divisor of both

[1] This symbol denotes the *absolute* value of r_2.   If $x \geqq 0$, then $|x| = x$; if $x \leqq 0$, then $|x| = -x$.   Thus $|2| = |-2| = 2$.

r_1 and r_2 is a divisor of r_l. For this reason r_l is called the *highest common factor*[1] of r_1 and r_2.

From (3.2) r_l is a linear, homogeneous expression in its two predecessors r_{l-1}, r_{l-2}. Since the same is true of r_{l-1}, r_l is a linear homogeneous expression in r_{l-2}, r_{l-3}. By repeated substitution, therefore, we get

$$(3.3) \qquad\qquad r_1 x + r_2 y = r_l,$$

a relation of great importance. The coefficients x, y are integers because they are formed by multiplication and addition of integers.

THEOREM 3.1.—*Every pair of integers, one of which is different from zero, has a uniquely determined highest common factor which satisfies* (3.3), *where x, y are integers.*

If r_1 and r_2 are relatively prime, $r_l = +1$, so that relation (3.3) becomes

$$(3.4) \qquad\qquad r_1 x + r_2 y = 1.$$

Moreover, if integers r_1, r_2, x, y satisfy (3.4), any integer dividing both r_1 and r_2 divides 1 so that the highest common factor is 1. Hence we have

THEOREM 3.2.—*The equation* $ax + by = 1$ *with integral coefficients a, b has a solution in integers x, y if and only if a and b are relatively prime.*

By means of this we can prove

THEOREM 3.3.—*If a product is divisible by a prime, at least one of its factors is divisible by that prime.*

Let fg be divisible by the prime p and let f be not divisible by p. Then f and p are relatively prime and there exist integers x, y satisfying $fx + py = 1$. Multiplication by g

---

[1] Note that it is positive.

gives $fgx + pgy = g$.   Since the left member is divisible by p, the right is also, and the theorem follows.

In the above proof it is not necessary that p be prime.   It suffices that p and f be relatively prime in order that p divide g. Hence we have the more general result:

Theorem 3.4.—*If h divides fg and is relatively prime to f, it divides g.*

The computation of (x, y) satisfying (3.4) will be illustrated by the equation

$$151x + 23y = 1.$$

The remainders and the quotients are

$$r \quad 151, \quad 23, \quad 13, \quad 10, \quad 3, \quad 1$$
$$q \qquad 6, \quad 1, \quad 1, \quad 3, \quad 3.$$

In finding x, y it is better to write the literal r's rather than their numerical values.   In terms of them relations (3.2) are

(3.5)
$$
\begin{aligned}
r_1 &= 6r_2 + r_3, \\
r_2 &= \quad r_3 + r_4, \\
r_3 &= \quad r_4 + r_5, \\
r_4 &= 3r_5 + 1.
\end{aligned}
$$

We must eliminate r_3, r_4, r_5 among these equations.   The result is

$$-7r_1 + 46r_2 = 1,$$

so that $x = -7$, $y = 46$ is a solution.

Although the method given for finding a solution of (3.4) leads to a unique solution, the equation always has an infinite number of solutions if it has one.   If two solutions are (x, y), (x_0, y_0), by substitution and subtraction we get

(3.6)
$$r_1(x - x_0) + r_2(y - y_0) = 0.$$

Since r_1, r_2 are relatively prime, by Theorem 3.4, $x - x_0$ is divisible by r_2, that is, we may write $x - x_0 = r_2t$, where t is an integer. Substitution in (3.6) gives $y - y_0 = -r_1t$. Substituting the values x, y so determined in (3.4) shows that they satisfy (3.4) for every integer t.

A general solution of (3.4) is accordingly

(3.7) $x_0 + r_2t,$ $y_0 - r_1t,$

where (x_0, y_0) is any particular solution. That resulting from the algorithm of the highest common divisor will of course serve.

If r_1, r_2, c are integers, the more general equation

(3.8) $r_1x + r_2y = c$

can have a solution in integers only if the highest common factor of r_1, r_2 divides c. We may suppose this common factor removed by division, so that r_1, r_2 are relatively prime. As before, relation (3.6) must hold between any two solutions and (3.7) gives a general solution, once a particular solution (x_0, y_0) is obtained. To find (x_0, y_0), let ξ, η be a solution of

$$r_1\xi + r_2\eta = 1.$$

Then $(\xi c, \eta c)$ obviously satisfies (3.8) and will serve as (x_0, y_0).

Illustrative Example.—Find in how many ways the sum of five dollars can be paid in dimes and quarters.

If x, y are respectively the number of dimes and quarters, then

$$10x + 25y = 500,$$

or

(3.9) $2x + 5y = 100.$

The solution of this is accomplished by means of the equation

$$2\xi + 5\eta = 1.$$

Here, as often is the case, a particular solution $(-2, 1)$ is readily determined by inspection. A particular solution of (3.9) is accordingly

(-200, 100), and the general solution is

$$x = -200 + 5t, \qquad y = 100 - 2t.$$

From the nature of the problem, x and y must be non-negative. Hence the integer t must satisfy $40 \leqq t \leqq 50$. There are accordingly just eleven values of t giving admissible (x, y).

EXERCISES

Apply Euclid's division algorithm to the following quotients:

3.1. $\dfrac{272}{368}$.   **3.2.** $\dfrac{-53}{71}$.   **3.3.** $\dfrac{275}{407}$.

3.4. What is the least common multiple of two integers? Find the least common multiple of 36 and 15.

3.5. In how many ways can a dollar be paid in nickels and dimes?

3.6. A man has a large tub, and two measures of capacity 3 quarts and 5 quarts, respectively. How can he measure exactly one quart with this apparatus?

4. Unique Factorization.—Let N be a positive composite number. To find the primes which divide it, we need only try the positive primes which are less than N. Although for large numbers this method is laborious, it is theoretically possible for any number.

Let p_1 be the least positive prime factor of N. N/p_1 may also be divisible by p_1, but it is divisible by no smaller positive prime. By trial we can find a positive integer e_1 such that $N/p_1^{e_1}$ is not divisible by p_1. Let p_2 be the smallest positive prime divisor of $N/p_1^{e_1}$ and let $N/(p_1^{e_1}p_2^{e_2})$ be not divisible by p_2. Continuing, we find

$$(4.1) \qquad N = p_1^{e_1}p_2^{e_2} \cdots p_m^{e_m},$$

where the p's are distinct, positive primes satisfying

$$p_1 < p_2 < \cdots < p_m.$$

This representation is unique, that is, if also

$$N = q_1^{f_1}q_2^{f_2} \cdots q_n^{f_n},$$

we must have

$$m = n, \qquad p_i = q_i, \qquad e_i = f_i.$$

This is so because both p_1 and q_1 are the smallest positive prime dividing N. Hence $p_1 = q_1$. The other equations readily follow.

EXERCISES

Express the following in the form (4.1):

4.1. 36. **4.2.** 60. **4.3.** 120.

5. Congruences.—For some purposes the actual magnitude of an integer is of less importance than the remainder when it is divided by a second integer. For example, in $(-1)^n$, the essential is whether n is even or odd, that is, the value of the expression depends solely on the remainder when n is divided by 2, and n can be replaced by that remainder.

If the difference between a and b is divisible by m, we write

$$a \equiv b \ (\mathrm{mod} \ m),$$

a relation read "a is congruent to b modulo m." Clearly congruence is transitive: if $a \equiv b$ and $b \equiv c$, then $a \equiv c$. We also have

THEOREM 5.1.—*If $a \equiv b$ and $c \equiv d$ (mod m), then $a + c \equiv b + d$, $a - c \equiv b - d$, $ac \equiv bd$ (mod m).*

The proof is left to the reader. The theorem says that we may treat congruences to a *fixed* modulus very much as we do equations, except in the case of division, which presents some peculiarities. How division may be accomplished is stated in

THEOREM 5.2.—*If $na \equiv nb$ (mod m), then $a \equiv b$ (mod m/r), where r is the highest common factor of m and n.*

To prove the theorem, put $m = rm'$, where m', n are relatively prime. Since m divides $n(a - b)$, its factor m' divides

$n(a - b)$. By Theorem 3.4 m' divides $a - b$ since it is prime to n.

Theorem 5.2 amounts to the following: *We may divide a congruence by a number provided we divide the modulus by the highest factor it has in common with the number.*

EXERCISES

Solve the congruences:

5.1. $5x \equiv 1 \pmod{7}$. **5.2.** $3x \equiv 2 \pmod 5$. **5.3.** $4x \equiv 3 \pmod 9$.

6. Residues.—The Euclid division algorithm applied to a and a positive m gives

$$a = qm + r$$

with $0 \leqq r < m$. r is called the *residue* of a with respect to m. It is also called the result of reducing a modulo m. The possible values of r, namely, $0, 1, 2, \cdots, m - 1$ are said to form a *complete residue system* modulo m.

The number of residues in a complete system which are relatively prime to the modulus m is denoted by $\phi(m)$, called the *Euler ϕ-function* or the *totient*. The number 1 always accounts for one unit in $\phi(m)$.

To find a formula for $\phi(m)$, we first prove

Theorem 6.1.—*If m and n are relatively prime, then $\phi(mn) = \phi(m)\phi(n)$.*

A complete residue system mod mn is given by $mq + r$, if q ranges over a complete residue system mod n and r over a complete residue system mod m. To prove this, it is sufficient to show that (i) $mq + r$ assumes mn values; (ii) these values are distinct; and (iii) each value is less than mn. Statement (i) is obviously true. Suppose two of the values are equal: $mq + r = mq' + r'$. Then $m(q - q') + (r - r') = 0$ and $r - r'$ is divisible by m. This is impossible unless $r = r'$ and $q = q'$. Finally, the truth of (iii) is shown by adding the inequalities $r < m$, $mq \leqq m(n - 1)$.

The integer $mq + r$ is prime to m if, and only if, r is.   Hence there are $\phi(m)$ values of r which make $mq + r$ prime to m. Consider for any one of these values the set

(6.1) $r, \qquad m + r, \qquad 2m + r, \qquad \cdots, \qquad (n - 1)m + r.$

No two of these are congruent mod n.   For, if

$$am + r \equiv bm + r \pmod{n},$$

then $am \equiv bm$, $a \equiv b \pmod{n}$ by Theorem 5.2.   Since both a and b belong to a complete residue system mod n, this means $a = b$.   Hence (6.1) when reduced mod n gives a complete residue system mod n.   Exactly $\phi(n)$ of the residues will be prime to n.   If now r is allowed to vary through its $\phi(m)$ values, there are obtained among the set of integers between zero and $mn - 1$ exactly $\phi(m)\,\phi(n)$ which are prime to both m and n, and by Theorem 3.3 prime to the product mn. The theorem is therefore true as stated.

THEOREM 6.2.—*If p (>0) is prime, $\phi(p^e) = p^e - p^{e-1}$.*

The positive integers not exceeding p^e and not prime to it are the multiples of p

$$p, \qquad 2p, \qquad \cdots, \qquad p^{e-1}p.$$

Of these, there are p^{e-1}.   If this number is subtracted from the total number of positive integers not exceeding p^e, namely, p^e, the number of relatively prime integers results and Theorem 6.2 is seen to be true.

From Theorems 6.1, 6.2 and equation (4.1) we immediately infer

THEOREM 6.3.—*If $p_1, \cdots, p_n$ are the distinct positive prime factors of a positive N, then*

$$\phi(N) = N\left(1 - \frac{1}{p_1}\right) \cdots \left(1 - \frac{1}{p_n}\right).$$

EXERCISES

6.1. If p is prime,

$$1 + \phi(p) + \phi(p^2) + \cdots + \phi(p^e) = p^e.$$

6.2. If P is the product of the distinct prime factors common to m and n, then

$$\phi(P)\phi(mn) = P\phi(m)\phi(n).$$

6.3. If sums, differences, products and quotients are redefined as the residues mod m of their usual values, every complete residue system mod m is a ring and every complete residue system mod p, where p is a prime, is a field.

An excellent detailed account of the number system will be found in H. B. Fine's *College Algebra*, pp. 1–78. Additional material on number theory will be found in L. E. Dickson's *Introduction to the Theory of Numbers*, Chicago, 1929.

CHAPTER II

PERMUTATIONS

Before starting the development of our subject proper it is necessary for us to have at our disposal several working tools. The elementary theory of one of these will be developed in the present chapter.

7. Definitions and Notation.—Each of the symbols

(7.1)   123,   132,   213,   231,   312,   321

is called an *arrangement* of the symbols 1, 2, 3.

The operation of passing from one of these arrangements to another (or to the same one) is called a *permutation*.[1] It is denoted by placing the two arrangements in parentheses, with the first appearing above. Thus the permutation converting 123 into 312 is denoted by

$$(7.2) \qquad \begin{pmatrix} 1 & 2 & 3 \\ 3 & 1 & 2 \end{pmatrix}.$$

This means that 1 is replaced by 3, 2 by 1, and 3 by 2.

From this it is clear the order in which the columns are written in the above symbol is immaterial provided the partner of each number and the row in which it appears are unaltered. Thus there are six ways of writing (7.2):

---

[1] In the literature, both of the notions developed here go by the name "permutation." In an introductory account, however, it seems well to emphasize the difference in nature by a difference in name.

15

$$\begin{pmatrix} 1 & 2 & 3 \\ 3 & 1 & 2 \end{pmatrix} = \begin{pmatrix} 1 & 3 & 2 \\ 3 & 2 & 1 \end{pmatrix} = \begin{pmatrix} 2 & 1 & 3 \\ 1 & 3 & 2 \end{pmatrix} = \begin{pmatrix} 2 & 3 & 1 \\ 1 & 2 & 3 \end{pmatrix} = \begin{pmatrix} 3 & 1 & 2 \\ 2 & 3 & 1 \end{pmatrix}$$
$$= \begin{pmatrix} 3 & 2 & 1 \\ 2 & 1 & 3 \end{pmatrix}.$$

The reader should verify that each of these replaces 1 by 3, 2 by 1, and 3 by 2.

The permutation (7.2) can be applied not only to (7.1), but to any expression involving the symbols 1, 2, 3. Thus the result of applying it to the subscripts of $x_1x_2 + x_3x_4$ is

$$x_3x_1 + x_2x_4.$$

Moreover, it can be regarded as leaving unaltered any expression involving none of the symbols 1, 2, 3.

A more concise and very useful notation for (7.2) is (132). In reading this, each letter is replaced by the one following it, the last being regarded as followed by the first. Thus the numbers are regarded as being on a circle, although it is easier to write them on a line, and (132) is accordingly called a *cycle*. Where we start reading the numbers on the circle is immaterial, provided the sense of description is fixed. We have thus three ways of writing the cycle under consideration:

$$(132) = (321) = (213).$$

The foregoing also applies when the n symbols 1, 2, $\cdots$, n are considered. Thus we have

$$\begin{pmatrix} 1 & 2 & 3 & \cdots & n \\ 2 & 3 & 4 & \cdots & 1 \end{pmatrix} = (123 \cdots n).$$

The number of letters in a cycle is its *period*. A cycle involving only two symbols is called a *transposition*.

Let us see what the permutation

(7.3) $$\begin{pmatrix} 1 & 2 & 3 & 4 \\ 2 & 1 & 4 & 3 \end{pmatrix}$$

becomes in terms of the shorter notation. Since 1 goes into 2 and 2 into 1, those symbols form a cycle (12) by themselves. Similarly, 3, 4 form the cycle (34). We write the whole as (12)(34).

When

$$\begin{pmatrix} 1 & 2 & 3 & 4 \\ 1 & 3 & 4 & 2 \end{pmatrix}$$

is reduced to cycles, 1 forms a cycle by itself, which, however, is not written; it is understood that any symbol not appearing in a permutation symbol is left unaltered by that permutation. Thus the above is written (234). If all the symbols are left unaltered, it is customary to denote the permutation by the symbol 1 *without* parentheses. This permutation is called the *identity*.

EXERCISES

Reduce to the form involving cycles.

7.1. $\begin{pmatrix} 1 & 2 & 3 & 4 & 5 & 6 \\ 2 & 6 & 4 & 3 & 1 & 5 \end{pmatrix}$.   **7.2.** $\begin{pmatrix} 1 & 2 & 3 & 4 & 5 & 6 & 7 \\ 4 & 6 & 5 & 7 & 3 & 2 & 1 \end{pmatrix}$.

8. Products of Permutations.—It is often convenient to represent permutations by letters $S, T, \cdots$. There is a single permutation which will produce the same result as applying S first and then applying T to the result. It is represented by the product ST, that is, when permutation symbols are multiplied, the permutations are to be performed successively *in the order indicated*. The expression of (7.3) as (12)(34) is in harmony with the definition just made, and in general when cycles have no letter in common, their multiplication amounts merely to their juxtaposition.

But if the cycles have a letter in common, simplification of the product is possible and advantageous. Thus in the case of the product (12)(23), the 1 is carried into 2 by the first factor and the 2 is subsequently carried into 3 by the second. Thus the 1 is carried into 3 by the product. The 3 is unaltered by the first and carried into 2 by the second, so that 3 is carried into 2 by the product. Finally, 2 is carried into 1 by the first factor and 1 is unaltered by the second, so that 2 is carried into 1 by the product. Therefore $(12)(23) = (132)$. Similarly, by tracing the history of each letter we find

$$(123)(245)(346) = (163)(245).$$

For the 1 becomes 2 by the first, 2 becomes 4 by the second, and 4 becomes 6 by the third. Thus 1 becomes 6, and we start a cycle $(16 \cdots)$. The next letter to go in the cycle is what 6 becomes: 6 into 6, 6 into 6, 6 into 3. The history of 3 is: 3 into 1, 1 into 1, 1 into 1. Since 3 becomes 1, we close the cycle and start another with any letter not yet accounted for. This gives the second cycle. The process is in general to be continued until all the letters are exhausted. Here the end is reached after two cycles have been found.

The identity (Sec. 7) satisfies $1 \cdot S = S \cdot 1 = S$, so that it behaves like the integer 1 under multiplication.

EXERCISES

Perform the indicated multiplications:

8.1. $(123)(13)$.   **8.2.** $(13)(123)$.   **8.3.** $(132)(12)(13)$.

8.4. $(1234)(456)(126)$.   **8.5.** $(12)(324)(416)$.

9. Multiplication Not Commutative.

—Unlike the integers, the set of permutation symbols does not satisfy (1.4), that is, the multiplication of permutations is not in general commutative, as the following example shows:

$$(12)(23) = (132), \qquad (23)(12) = (123).$$

The multiplication, however, is readily shown to be associative.

The multiplication of two *particular permutations*, however, may be commutative. In this case they are called *permutable*.

Any two cycles having no letter in common are permutable.
Thus $(12)(34) = (34)(12)$.

Although the two transpositions $(ij)(jk)$, in which i, j, k are
all distinct, are not permutable, there is a way of changing
the position one of them occupies in a product, that is, one can
be carried over the other. This is accomplished by the easily
proved identity

$$(9.1) \qquad\qquad (ij)(jk) = (jk)(ik),$$

both sides of which are (ikj).

10. Powers.—As in the case of an ordinary quantity, S^2 is
used as an abbreviation for SS, S^3 for SSS, etc. We readily
see that $(1234)^2 = (13)(24)$. This is an example of the
following rule.

*In the kth power of a cycle the letter replacing any given letter
is the kth letter following it in the cycle.*

For $k = 1$, any letter a is replaced by the letter, say b,
immediately following it in the cycle. A second application
of the permutation will replace b by that immediately following b, that is, by the second following a, and so on.

THEOREM 10.1.—*If C is a cycle and p its period, then
$C^p = 1$ and no lower positive power is 1.*

For C^p by the above rule replaces each letter by the pth
from it, that is, by itself; whereas any lower power replaces it
by some other letter.

If $C_1 = (123 \cdots n)$, $C_2 = (n \cdots 321)$, where $n \cdots$
321 denotes $123 \cdots n$ written in reverse order, we clearly
have $C_1 C_2 = C_2 C_1 = 1$, so that each of these cycles cancels
the effect of the other. For this reason, each is called the
inverse of the other and we write $C_1 = C_2^{-1}$, $C_2 = C_1^{-1}$. Note
that inverse cycles are permutable, although they involve
the same letters. The usual way of writing the inverse is

($1n \cdot \cdot \cdot 32$). The rule for writing down the inverse of a cycle in this form should be apparent.

Consider the permutations

(10.1) $$S = C_1 C_2 \cdot \cdot \cdot C_r,$$

where the C's are cycles no two of which have a letter in common, and

(10.2) $$T = C_r^{-1} \cdot \cdot \cdot C_2^{-1} C_1^{-1}.$$

Then $ST = C_1 C_2 \cdot \cdot \cdot C_r C_r^{-1} \cdot \cdot \cdot C_2^{-1} C_1^{-1}$. The associative law allows parentheses to be placed around $C_r C_r^{-1}$. It then equals 1 and can be suppressed. Repetition of this process gives $ST = 1$. In the same way, $TS = 1$. Hence S and T are called *inverses*, a definition in harmony with that previously given for cycles. We write $T = S^{-1}$.

If the C's in (10.1) and (10.2) are interpreted as arbitrary permutations, the result

$$ST = TS = 1$$

is still valid. Hence we have

THEOREM 10.2.—*The inverse of a product is the product of the inverses written in reverse order.*

If the theorem is applied to $S^p = S \cdot S \cdot \cdot \cdot S$, we find $(S^p)^{-1} = (S^{-1})^p$. If we write as a definition $(S^{-1})^p = S^{-p}$, then $S^p S^{-p} = 1$. If in addition we put $S^0 = 1$, the law $S^p S^q = S^{p+q}$, only known previously to hold for positive values of p, q, is readily proved true for all integers.

THEOREM 10.3.—*If S is a permutation of period p, then $S^x = 1$ if and only if $x \equiv 0$ (mod p).*

We shall prove the theorem first for a cycle C of period p. If the residue r of x (mod p) is positive, then $C^r = 1$ with $0 < r < p$, a result seen above to be impossible. Hence $r = 0$.

Conversely, if the residue is zero, the relation is $C^0 = 1$, and the theorem is true for a cycle.

If the expression (10.1) for the permutation S contains two or more cycles whose periods are $p_1, \cdots, p_r$, respectively, the period of S has not yet been defined. Let the least common multiple P of $p_1, \cdots, p_r$ be called the period of S. We wish next to show that with this definition Theorem 10.3 is true for permutations in general. Since the cycles are permutable and $P \equiv 0 \pmod{p_i}$, we have from Theorem 10.1

$$S^P = C_1^P \cdots C_r^P = 1,$$

a result analogous to that for cycles.

Conversely, if

$$C_1^x \cdots C_r^x = 1,$$

the relation is equivalent to

$$C_1^x = 1, \quad \cdots, \quad C_r^x = 1,$$

since the cycles have no letter in common. Hence $x \equiv 0 \pmod{p_i}$, that is, x is divisible by all the p's and hence by their least common multiple P. Therefore the theorem is completely demonstrated. At the same time we note the

DEFINITION 10.1.—*The period of a product of cycles no two of which have a letter in common is the least common multiple of the periods of the cycles.*

Thus $(12)(34)$ and $(12)(345)$ have periods 2 and 6, respectively.

EXERCISES

10.1. Write out all the distinct powers of $S = (12345)$, and determine the inverse and period of each.

10.2. Treat $T = (12)(345)$ in the same way.

Find the inverses of the following:

10.3. (12).   **10.4.** (123).   **10.5.** $(12)(34)$.

10.6. $(123)(456)$.   **10.7.** $(123)(425)$.

11. Factorization into Transpositions.—The following identity is readily verified by multiplication of the right side:

$$(11.1) \qquad (123 \, \cdots \, n) = (12)(13) \, \cdots \, (1n).$$

Hence, *every permutation can be expressed as a product of transpositions.* Note that the factors on the right of (11.1) are not permutable.

The factorization is not unique. We also have

$$(123 \, \cdots \, n) = (23)(24) \, \cdots \, (2n)(21),$$

and similarly any one of the n letters can be made to play the role of 1 in equation (11.1).

The number of factors on the right of (11.1) can be made to vary. Thus

$$(123) = (12)(13) = (24)(12)(13)(34).$$

The number of transpositions for a given permutation, however, is always even or always odd, as will be proved in the next section. Accordingly, the permutation is called *even* or *odd*.

It is apparent from (11.1) that the cycle of period n is even or odd according as n is odd or even. This can be expressed by saying that a cycle and its period have *opposite parity*.

12. Even and Odd Permutations.—The important and useful fact mentioned at the end of the last section can be proved as follows. Let S be the product of an even number of transpositions and T be the product of an odd number of transpositions. Then if $S = T$, we have $ST^{-1} = 1$, and the identity is equal to an odd number of transpositions. This will be a contradiction if we show the truth of

THEOREM 12.1.—*If a product of transpositions is the identity, the number of transpositions is even.*

The theorem is true for two letters because by Theorem 10.3 the equation $(12)^p = 1$ implies that p is even.

Consider a particular transposition (12) in the general case of n letters. It may occur in several places, but these may all

be replaced by a single expression $(12)^p$ in the following way.
(12) is permutable with any transposition containing neither
a 1 nor a 2. When it is to the right of a transposition containing one of these digits, it can be moved to the left by means
of (9.1), that is, by means of the identities

$$(1k)(12) = (12)(k2), \qquad (2k)(12) = (12)(1k).$$

This process leaves the number of transpositions unaltered.
We may accordingly assume that (12) occurs only on the
extreme left in the form $(12)^p$. Treat $(13), \cdots, (1n)$
successively in the same way. Thus we obtain a relation of
the form

(12.1) $(12)^{p_2}(13)^{p_3} \cdots (1n)^{p_n}U = 1,$

where U is a product of transpositions not involving 1. If
p_2 is odd, $(12)^{p_2} = (12)$. The transformation on the left
then carries 1 into some different letter, and cannot be the
identity. Hence p_2 is even and $(12)^{p_2}$ can be omitted from
the left member of equation (12.1) without invalidating the
equation or changing the parity of the number of transpositions. The same thing is true for the other p's, and $U = 1$.
If we assume the truth of the theorem for $n - 1$ letters, we
infer its truth in general.

EXERCISE

12.1. Reduce by the above method

$$(12)(23)(12)(24)(14)(12)(13)(14).$$

13. Symmetric and Alternating Groups.

—From elementary
algebra there are $n!$ permutations on n letters. The totality
of these is called the *symmetric group of degree* n.

Let the even permutations in the symmetric group be

(13.1) $S_1, \qquad S_2, \qquad \cdots, \qquad S_k.$

Let these be multiplied by any odd permutation T to give

(13.2) $S_1T, \qquad S_2T, \qquad \cdots, \qquad S_kT.$

These are all distinct: if $S_iT = S_jT$, by multiplication with T^{-1} on the right we conclude $S_i = S_j$. The permutations (13.2), moreover, are all odd. Hence there are at least as many odd permutations as even. If the S's be interpreted as all the odd permutations and the T as odd, then (13.2) are all even, and so we find there are at least as many even as odd. Hence exactly half of the permutations are even and half are odd.

The even permutations on n letters are said to form the *alternating group of degree* n. It contains $\frac{1}{2}(n!)$ permutations.

Every permutation belongs to an infinite number of symmetric groups. Thus (12) belongs to the symmetric groups of degree 2, 3, 4, $\cdots$. When a permutation is regarded as belonging to a symmetric group of given degree n, it is said to be of *degree* n. Thus the degree of a permutation is a relative term.

Let all permutations of degree n be written on a line as

$$(13.3) \qquad S_1, \qquad S_2, \qquad \cdots, \qquad S_l \qquad (l = n!).$$

If T is any permutation of degree n, the permutations

$$(13.4) \qquad S_1T, \qquad S_2T, \qquad \cdots, \qquad S_lT$$

are all distinct, as was the case in (13.2), and they are therefore the same as (13.3) except possibly for the order in which they are written.

EXERCISES

13.1. Write out (13.1) and (13.2) for the cases $n = 3$, $n = 4$.
13.2. Write out (13.3) and (13.4) for the case $n = 3$.
13.3. Classify as even or odd the permutations in Exercises 8.

For further information about permutations the reader may consult H. F. Blichfeldt's *Finite Collineation Groups*, Chicago, 1917, pp. 29–62; E. Netto's *Theory of Substitutions and Its Applications to Algebra*, Ann Arbor, 1892; and E. Netto's *Lehrbuch der Combinatorik*, Leipzig, 1927.

CHAPTER III

DETERMINANTS

14. Definition.—The expression

$$ad - bc$$

is a determinant of order 2. A handy way of tabulating its four elements a, b, c, d is to place them in the form of a square

(14.1)
$$\begin{array}{cc} a & b \\ c & d \end{array}.$$

This array is called a *square matrix*. a, d lie on the *main*, b, c on the *secondary diagonal*. The determinant associated with this matrix is then the product of the elements on its main diagonal minus the product of the elements on its secondary diagonal.

A more instructive way of writing the elements in (14.1) is

$$\begin{array}{cc} a_1^1 & a_2^1 \\ a_1^2 & a_2^2 \end{array},$$

the upper index indicating the row (horizontal), and the lower index the column (vertical). The determinant is then

(14.2)
$$a_1^1 a_2^2 - a_2^1 a_1^2.$$

The second term can be thought of as arising from the first by subjecting the subscripts on the first term to the transposition (12) and changing the sign. The first term can be thought of as arising by subjecting its subscripts to the identity permutation.

25

The process of subjecting a chosen set of indices in an expression to a permutation and multiplying by ± 1 according as the permutation is even or odd is called *applying the signed permutation.*

Thus the determinant treated above arises from $a_1^1 a_2^2$ by subjecting its subscripts to all the signed permutations of degree 2 and adding the results. The advantage of this form of the definition is that it is easily generalized as follows.

The determinant of order n with elements a_j^i is the polynomial obtained from $a_1^1 a_2^2 \cdots a_n^n$ by subjecting its subscripts to all signed permutations of degree n and adding the results.

A determinant is usually denoted by placing vertical bars around the matrix from which it arises.

The determinant

$$(14.3) \qquad \begin{vmatrix} a_1^1 & a_2^1 & a_3^1 \\ a_1^2 & a_2^2 & a_3^2 \\ a_1^3 & a_2^3 & a_3^3 \end{vmatrix}$$

is accordingly

$$(14.4) \quad a_1^1 a_2^2 a_3^3 - a_1^1 a_3^2 a_2^3 + a_2^1 a_3^2 a_1^3 - a_2^1 a_1^2 a_3^3 + a_3^1 a_1^2 a_2^3 - a_3^1 a_2^2 a_1^3.$$

There are rules for writing down this expression from the square array, but their complicated nature leads us to omit them. As we shall see presently, there are efficient methods for evaluating determinants directly from the square array.

The term $a_1^1 a_2^2 \cdots a_n^n$ from which the others are obtained is called the *leader.*

It should be noted that it is immaterial whether we apply the permutation to the subscripts or the superscripts. Thus the second term of (14.2) is $-a_1^2 a_2^1$, if signed (12) is applied to the superscripts. It is the same as before because the a's obey the commutative law of multiplication (1.4). In the general case, since the terms in the polynomial depend only on the relative positions of the indices, the same determinant arises if the permutations are all applied to the superscripts, rather than to the subscripts. Hence we have the fundamental result contained in

THEOREM 14.1.—*A determinant is unaltered by interpreting its rows as the corresponding columns and vice versa. Consequently any theorem on determinants remains true if the words "row" and "column" are interchanged in its statement.*

As a consequence, we shall in the sequel prove most of the results for rows. We, moreover, shall often not even bother to state the corresponding results for columns.

The result of interchanging rows and columns in a matrix or a determinant is called the *transpose*.

EXERCISES

14.1. Write the expression like (14.4) for a determinant of order 4.

14.2. Find the sign of the term containing the elements on the secondary diagonal of a determinant of order n.

15. Elementary Transformations.—The signed transposition (12) applied to the subscripts in (14.4) gives

$$-a_2^1 a_1^2 a_3^3 + a_2^1 a_3^2 a_1^3 - a_1^1 a_3^2 a_2^3 + a_1^1 a_2^2 a_3^3 - a_3^1 a_2^2 a_1^3 + a_3^1 a_1^2 a_2^3,$$

whose terms are the same as those of (14.4), although written in a different order. Hence the determinant is unaltered, or as we shall say, *invariant* under the process, which is equivalent to interchanging its first two columns and changing its sign. This result is a special case of the first of the transformations written below.

THEOREM 15.1.—*A determinant is invariant under the following elementary transformations:*

(i) *Interchanging two rows and multiplying the determinant by* -1.

(ii) *Multiplying every element in a fixed row by the same non-zero quantity and the determinant by its reciprocal.*

(iii) *Replacing every element in a fixed row by the sum of itself and a fixed multiple of the element on a different fixed row and the same column.*

(iv) *Writing all the rows as the corresponding columns.*

(v) *The transformations obtained from the above by interchanging the words "row" and "column."*

Before studying the proof of this theorem, the reader should apply it to determinant (14.3) and verify that the value is unaltered in each case by writing out the determinant.

To prove (i) of this theorem, let the determinant be D and consider its leader

$$(15.1) \qquad\qquad a_1^1 a_2^2 \cdots a_n^n.$$

D results by applying the signed permutations (13.3) of the symmetric group of degree n to (15.1) and adding. Let the result of applying the signed permutation T to D be denoted by D'. Then D' is found by applying signed (13.4) to (15.1). Since (13.3) and (13.4) are the same except possibly for the order in which they are written, we must have $D = D'$.

If in particular $T = (ij)$ and the permutations are applied to the *superscripts*, T interchanges the ith and jth rows, and D has been proved invariant under (i).

If two rows of the determinant are identical, their interchange obviously leaves the determinant unaltered. Hence we have both $D = D'$ and $D = -D'$, and therefore $D = 0$. This combined with (ii) gives

THEOREM 15.2.—*If two rows of a determinant are identical or proportional, the determinant is zero.*

Part (iv) is contained in Theorem 14.1. Part (v) will follow from (ii) and (iii) whose proof will be given after some additional tools are at our disposal.

16. Algebraic Complement.—Since any one of the integers 1, 2, $\cdots$, n occurs as a superscript once and only once in each term of a determinant, we have the fundamental result:

THEOREM 16.1.—*The determinant is a linear homogeneous expression in the elements on any given row or column.*

Thus when the superscript 2 is considered, (14.4) can be written

$$(16.1) \quad -a_1^2(a_2^1a_3^3 - a_3^1a_2^3) + a_2^2(a_1^1a_3^3 - a_3^1a_1^3) - a_3^2(a_1^1a_2^3 - a_2^1a_1^3),$$

that is, as a linear homogeneous expression in the elements a_1^2, a_2^2, a_3^2 on its second row.

Definition.—The *algebraic complement* of an element is the polynomial which multiplies it when the determinant is written as a linear expression in the elements on its row. Thus the algebraic complement of a_1^2 in (14.4) is $-(a_2^1a_3^3 - a_3^1a_2^3)$. The algebraic complement of a_j^i is denoted by A_i^j.

EXERCISE

16.1. Write the algebraic complement of every element in determinant (16.1).

17. Minors.—It will be noted that the expression in parentheses in the illustration just given is the determinant

$$\begin{vmatrix} a_2^1 & a_3^1 \\ a_2^3 & a_3^3 \end{vmatrix}$$

and that the latter can be obtained from (14.3) by striking out the row and column in which a_1^2 occurs. This is a special case of the following

Definition.—The determinant arising by deleting the row and column in which a given element occurs is called the *minor* of that element in the original determinant. The minor of a_j^i is denoted by α_i^j.

We shall next prove

THEOREM 17.1.—*The algebraic complement and the minor are related by*

(17.1) $$A_i^j = (-1)^{i+j} \alpha_i^j,$$

that is, the algebraic complement is the minor or the minor with its sign changed according as the sum of the row and column on which the element occurs is even or odd.

To carry out the proof, we get the leader of the minor by writing down $n - 1$ a's and putting on them superscripts which are $1, 2, \cdots, n$ in natural order with i left out. Similarly for subscripts, that is, we ignore i as a superscript and j as a subscript. Thus the minor of a_3^2 in a determinant of order 4 has leader

$$a_1^1 a_2^3 a_4^4.$$

A permutation which gives superscripts and subscripts this relative arrangement is that which interchanges the superscript i successively with each superscript preceding it, that is, performs $(i\ i - 1)(i\ i - 2) \cdots (i\ 1)$ on the superscripts, and subsequently interchanges the subscript j with each that precedes it. This permutation being obviously equivalent to $i + j - 2$ transpositions, the desired result follows.

It should be noted that on the main diagonal $i = j$, so that the minor and algebraic complement are equal for all elements on the main diagonal.

EXERCISE

17.1. Find the minors of all elements in determinant (16.1) and verify that they are related to the algebraic complements obtained in Exercise 16.1 by formulas (17.1).

18. The Summation Convention.—A sum like

(18.1) $$a_1 x^1 + a_2 x^2 + \cdots + a_n x^n$$

can be written

$$\sum_{i=1}^{n} a_i x^i.$$

This means that the index i is to be given successively each integral value from 1 to n and the results are to be added. Very often the summed index is repeated, as above. In such cases, the Σ can be omitted provided we agree that repeated indices are to be summed. Thus it is convenient to write (18.1) as

$$a_i x^i.$$

If the range of the index i is not obvious, it must be indicated in some such manner as

$$a_i x^i \qquad (i = 1, 2, \cdots, n).$$

In our application of this convention to determinants, however, the range will always be the same and will not have to be indicated.

EXERCISES

Write out in full the following expressions.

18.1.	$a_i x^i$	$(i = 1, 2, 3, 4)$.
18.2.	$a_{ij} x^i x^j$	$(i = 1, 2, 3)$.
18.3.	$a_{ij} x^i y^j$	$(i = 1, 2, 3, 4)$.

19. The Deltas and Epsilons.[1]—The Kronecker delta δ_j^i is defined to be one or zero according as its indices represent the same or different positive integers. Thus

$$\delta_1^1 = \delta_2^2 = 1, \qquad \delta_2^1 = \delta_3^2 = 0.$$

The two symbols

$$\epsilon^{i_1 i_2 \cdots i_n}, \qquad \epsilon_{i_1 i_2 \cdots i_n}$$

[1] The epsilons were first systematically employed by O. Veblen. *Cf. Invariants of Quadratic Differential Forms*, Cambridge, 1927, pp. 11–12.

have values defined as follows: the value is $+1$ if $i_1 i_2 \cdots i_n$ is an even arrangement of $12 \cdots n$; it is -1 if $i_1 i_2 \cdots i_n$ is an odd arrangement of $12 \cdots n$; and it is zero if $i_1 i_2 \cdots i_n$ is not any arrangement of $12 \cdots n$.

In terms of the ϵ's, the determinant a_j^i can be written in two forms:

$$(19.1) \qquad \epsilon^{i_1 i_2 \cdots i_n} a_{i_1}^1 a_{i_2}^2 \cdots a_{i_n}^n, \qquad \epsilon_{i_1 i_2 \cdots i_n} a_1^{i_1} a_2^{i_2} \cdots a_n^{i_n}.$$

Thus the determinant of order three is

$$\epsilon^{ijk} a_i^1 a_j^2 a_k^3 = \epsilon^{123} a_1^1 a_2^2 a_3^3 + \epsilon^{132} a_1^1 a_3^2 a_2^3 + \epsilon^{231} a_2^1 a_3^2 a_1^3 + \epsilon^{213} a_2^1 a_1^2 a_3^3$$
$$+ \epsilon^{312} a_3^1 a_1^2 a_2^3 + \epsilon^{321} a_3^1 a_2^2 a_1^3.$$

This reduces to the expression formerly given because

$$\epsilon^{123} = \epsilon^{231} = \epsilon^{312} = 1, \qquad \epsilon^{132} = \epsilon^{213} = \epsilon^{321} = -1.$$

EXERCISES

Prove the following identities:

19.1. $\delta_i^i = n.$ **19.2.** $\delta_j^i \delta_k^j = \delta_k^i.$ **19.3.** $\delta_j^i x^j = x^i.$

19.4. $a_{ij} \delta_k^i \delta_l^j = a_{kl}.$

19.5. Prove $\epsilon_{ij} = \delta_i^1 \delta_j^2 - \delta_i^2 \delta_j^1.$

19.6. By using (19.1) prove that if a, b are determinants with elements a_j^i, b_j^i, then $ab = c$, where c is the determinant with $c_k^i = a_j^i b_k^j$. This is the multiplication theorem for determinants. By it the product of two determinants of order n is expressed as a determinant of the same order.

20. Expansion of a Determinant.—We shall show that

$$(20.1) \qquad\qquad a_j^i A_k^j = \delta_k^i a,$$

where a (without indices) denotes the determinant with elements a_j^i. If $i = k$, the result follows because it amounts to the definition of the algebraic complements. The left member for $i \neq k$ arises from its value for $i = k$ by replacing the kth row by the ith row. Since this gives a determinant with two identical rows, by Theorem 15.2 the left member is zero and is therefore equal to the right.

By interchanging rows and columns we have, of course, the companion formula

(20.2) $a_k^j A_j^i = \delta_k^i a.$

When $i = k$, formula (20.1) gives the *expansion* of the determinant in terms of the elements of the kth row, and (20.2) its expansion in terms of the elements of the kth column.

The following are examples of expansion in terms of the elements of the second row and third column, respectively.

$$\begin{vmatrix} a & b & c \\ d & e & f \\ g & h & k \end{vmatrix} = -d \begin{vmatrix} b & c \\ h & k \end{vmatrix} + e \begin{vmatrix} a & c \\ g & k \end{vmatrix} - f \begin{vmatrix} a & b \\ g & h \end{vmatrix},$$

$$\begin{vmatrix} a & b & c \\ d & e & f \\ g & h & k \end{vmatrix} = +c \begin{vmatrix} d & e \\ g & h \end{vmatrix} - f \begin{vmatrix} a & b \\ g & h \end{vmatrix} + k \begin{vmatrix} a & b \\ d & e \end{vmatrix}.$$

A rule helpful in determining the sign to be placed before the minor in order to have the algebraic complement is: starting in the upper left corner with plus, proceed to the element involved by horizontal and vertical steps counting the elements alternately plus and minus. Thus the signs in the above for c, d, f can be determined by the paths

$$\begin{vmatrix} + & - & + \\ & & \\ & & \end{vmatrix}, \begin{vmatrix} + \\ - \\ \end{vmatrix} \qquad , \begin{vmatrix} + \\ - & + & - \\ \end{vmatrix}.$$

A consequence of this is that the signs for the elements on any row or column alternate.

EXERCISE

20.1. Expand the determinant of order 4 with elements a_j^i in terms of its second column.

21. Completion of the Proofs for the Elementary Transformations.—We return to complete the proof of Theorem 15.1.

Multiplying by λ the elements in the ith row of the determinant a amounts to replacing a_j^i in (20.1) by λa_j^i. If the left member is subsequently divided by λ, its value, and hence that of the determinant a, is clearly left unaltered. Hence (ii) is true.

Consider k in (20.1) to have the same value as i. Replacing a_j^i by $a_j^i + \lambda a_j^l$, for $l \neq i$, in (20.1) gives

$$(21.1) \qquad a_j^i A_k^j + \lambda a_j^l A_k^j.$$

The second of these terms is zero because $a_j^l A_k^j$ is a determinant whose ith and lth rows have identical elements since $a_j^l A_k^j$ arises from $a_j^i A_k^j$ by replacing its ith row by its lth. Hence (iii) is true, and Theorem 15.1 has been completely demonstrated.

22. Evaluation of Determinants.—The easiest way to evaluate a determinant in general is to apply to it elementary transformations in the manner illustrated by the following example:

$$\begin{vmatrix} 2 & 3 & 5 \\ 2 & 2 & 3 \\ 3 & 2 & 5 \end{vmatrix} = \frac{1}{4} \begin{vmatrix} 2 & 6 & 10 \\ 2 & 4 & 6 \\ 3 & 4 & 10 \end{vmatrix} = \frac{1}{4} \begin{vmatrix} 2 & 0 & 10 \\ 2 & -2 & 6 \\ 3 & -5 & 10 \end{vmatrix}$$

$$= \frac{1}{4} \begin{vmatrix} 2 & 0 & 0 \\ 2 & -2 & -4 \\ 3 & -5 & -5 \end{vmatrix} = \frac{1}{4} \begin{vmatrix} 2 & 0 & 0 \\ 2 & -2 & 0 \\ 3 & -5 & 5 \end{vmatrix} = -5$$

In the above reduction, the object is to get all elements, except possibly one, on the first row equal to zero by applying (iii) of Theorem 15.1. The first step is to multiply the second and third columns by 2 in order to make their top elements multiples of the 2 which appears in the upper left corner. The factor $\frac{1}{4}$ is introduced to compensate in accordance with (ii) of Theorem 15.1. The second step is to replace the second column by itself minus 3 times the first. The third step is to replace the third column by itself minus 5 times the first. The same operation is then to be applied to the determinant of order two in the lower right corner. Its third column is replaced by itself minus 2 times the second. As only zeros occur in the corresponding places on the first row, the first row is unaltered in the process. There is finally obtained a determinant with nothing but zeros above its main diagonal. It can be easily evaluated as the product of the elements on its main diagonal (see Theorem 22.1 below).

There are many ways in which the work may be shortened. The two zeros can be introduced on the first row in a single step. If there is a 1 anywhere in the determinant, the preliminary multiplications can be avoided. It is also easy at times to introduce a 1. All these points will be illustrated in a second working of the above example.

$$\begin{vmatrix} 2 & 3 & 5 \\ 2 & 2 & 3 \\ 3 & 2 & 5 \end{vmatrix} = \begin{vmatrix} 2 & 3 & 3 \\ 2 & 2 & 1 \\ 3 & 2 & 2 \end{vmatrix} = \begin{vmatrix} -4 & -3 & 0 \\ 2 & 2 & 1 \\ -1 & -2 & 0 \end{vmatrix}$$

$$= \begin{vmatrix} -4 & -3 & 0 \\ 0 & 0 & 1 \\ -1 & -2 & 0 \end{vmatrix} = \begin{vmatrix} -4 & 5 & 0 \\ 0 & 0 & 1 \\ -1 & 0 & 0 \end{vmatrix} = \begin{vmatrix} 0 & 5 & 0 \\ 0 & 0 & 1 \\ -1 & 0 & 0 \end{vmatrix}$$

$$= -\begin{vmatrix} 0 & 5 & 0 \\ 1 & 0 & 0 \\ 0 & 0 & -1 \end{vmatrix} = \begin{vmatrix} 1 & 0 & 0 \\ 0 & 5 & 0 \\ 0 & 0 & -1 \end{vmatrix} = -5.$$

The first step replaces the last column by itself minus the first. A 1 is thus introduced. The second row is next copied as it is, whereas the first is replaced by itself minus 3 times the second, and the third is replaced by itself minus 2 times the second. The 1 is next similarly employed to reduce the other two elements in the second row to zero. A second zero is then introduced into the second column by replacing the second column by itself minus 2 times the first. Replacing the first row by itself minus 4 times the third puts a second zero in the first row. Finally the first and third columns are interchanged, and then the first and second rows.

It should be clear that if all the elements on a row are zero except one element b, all the elements on the same column with b can be replaced by zeros without altering any other elements in the determinant: for, if c occurs in the column with b, replace c's row by itself minus c/b times b's row. Since all elements on b's row are zero except that in c's column, only c is affected by the replacement. From this we readily have the result:

THEOREM 22.1.—*If all the elements above (or below) the main diagonal are zero, the determinant reduces to its leader.*

For it can be reduced to a form in which all elements off the main diagonal are zero, so that any non-zero term must contain just the elements on the main diagonal.

A second method, which is to be recommended when the elements are letters, consists in expanding the determinant as in Sec. 20. Thus expansion in terms of the second column gives for the above example:

$$\begin{vmatrix} 2 & 3 & 5 \\ 2 & 2 & 3 \\ 3 & 2 & 5 \end{vmatrix} = -3\begin{vmatrix} 2 & 3 \\ 3 & 5 \end{vmatrix} + 2\begin{vmatrix} 2 & 5 \\ 3 & 5 \end{vmatrix} - 2\begin{vmatrix} 2 & 5 \\ 2 & 3 \end{vmatrix}$$
$$= -3(10-9) + 2(10-15) - 2(6-10)$$
$$= -3 - 10 + 8 = -5.$$

This method becomes involved as the order increases.

EXERCISES

Evaluate the following determinants both by using elementary transformations and by expanding.

22.1. $\begin{vmatrix} 1 & 1 \\ -1 & 1 \end{vmatrix}$.

22.2. $\begin{vmatrix} 0 & 1 & 1 \\ 1 & 0 & 1 \\ 1 & 1 & 0 \end{vmatrix}$.

22.3. $\begin{vmatrix} 1 & 2 & 3 \\ 4 & 5 & 6 \\ 7 & 8 & 9 \end{vmatrix}$.

22.4. $\begin{vmatrix} -2 & 3 & 4 \\ 3 & 4 & -2 \\ 5 & 6 & -3 \end{vmatrix}$.

$$\textbf{22.5.} \quad \begin{vmatrix} 2 & 3 & 4 \\ 3 & 2 & 3 \\ 4 & 3 & 2 \end{vmatrix}. \qquad\qquad \textbf{22.6.} \quad \begin{vmatrix} 0 & a & b \\ -a & 0 & c \\ -b & -c & 0 \end{vmatrix}.$$

$$\textbf{22.7.} \quad \begin{vmatrix} a & h & g \\ h & b & f \\ g & f & c \end{vmatrix}. \qquad\qquad \textbf{22.8.} \quad \begin{vmatrix} 1 & 1 & 1 & 1 \\ 1 & 2 & 2 & 2 \\ 1 & 2 & 3 & 3 \\ 1 & 2 & 3 & 4 \end{vmatrix}.$$

$$\textbf{22.9.} \quad \begin{vmatrix} 2 & 3 & 4 & 5 \\ 3 & -2 & 3 & 4 \\ 4 & 3 & 2 & 3 \\ 5 & 4 & 3 & -2 \end{vmatrix}. \qquad \textbf{22.10.} \quad \begin{vmatrix} 0 & a & b & c \\ -a & 0 & d & e \\ -b & -d & 0 & f \\ -c & -e & -f & 0 \end{vmatrix}.$$

23. Bordered Determinants.—Consider the determinant of order $n + 1$

$$(23.1) \qquad\qquad \begin{vmatrix} a_j^i & b^i \\ c_j & d \end{vmatrix} \qquad (i, j = 1, 2, \cdots, n),$$

where b^i, d form an $(n + 1)$th column and c_j, d an $(n + 1)$th row. It is said to arise by *bordering the determinant*

$$(23.2) \qquad\qquad\qquad | \ a_j^i \ | \qquad (i, j = 1, 2, \cdots, n).$$

Let us expand it in terms of the last row. The minor of c_j is a determinant of order n which can be obtained from (23.2) by omitting the jth column and then placing the column of b's on the right, or by replacing the jth column of (23.2) by the b's and multiplying by $(-1)^{n-j}$, since $n - j$ interchanges of adjacent columns will bring the b's into that position. By (20.1), the value of the minor is then

$$(-1)^{n-i} A_i^j b^i,$$

and the algebraic complement is this multiplied by $(-1)^{n+j+1}$, since c_j is in the $(n + 1)$th row and jth column of (23.1). The algebraic complement of d is, moreover, determinant (23.2), which we have called a. Hence we have

$$ad - A_i^j b^i c_j$$

as the value of the bordered determinant.

If the bordered determinant is zero, we have therefore

(23.3) $$ad = A_i^j b^i c_j.$$

24. Matrices.—A rectangular array of symbols is called a *matrix*. Square matrices have already been encountered in Sec. 14.

Consider any matrix. Fix the attention on k of its rows and k of its columns. If we erase all elements except those simultaneously on one of these rows and one of these columns, there is left a square array, whose determinant is called *a determinant of the matrix*.

Thus for $k = 1$ the matrix

$$\begin{matrix} a & b & c \\ d & e & f \end{matrix}$$

gives rise to the determinants

$$a, \quad b, \quad c, \quad d, \quad e, \quad f$$

and for $k = 2$ to

$$\begin{vmatrix} a & b \\ d & e \end{vmatrix}, \quad \begin{vmatrix} a & c \\ d & f \end{vmatrix}, \quad \begin{vmatrix} b & c \\ e & f \end{vmatrix}.$$

If all determinants of order $n + 1$ from a matrix are zero and some determinant of order n from it is different from zero, the matrix is said to have *rank n*.

Theorem 24.1.—*The rank of a matrix is invariant under elementary transformations.*

The foregoing result is obvious for transformations (iv) and (v) of Sec. 15 because every determinant of the matrix is subjected to an elementary transformation.

If (i), when applied to a matrix, is interpreted simply as interchanging two rows, it leaves the rank invariant.

Transformation (ii) is likewise seen to leave the rank unaltered, provided it is interpreted simply as multiplying the elements of a row by the same non-zero factor.

On the other hand, transformation (iii) applied to the matrix adds to a row of certain determinants equimultiples of some row not contained in those determinants and hence is not an elementary transformation of those determinants. In formula (21.1) the second expression no longer vanishes because it is a determinant with two identical rows; but if $a_j^i A_k^j$ is interpreted as a determinant of order greater than the rank of the matrix, so also is $a_j^l A_k^j$ and the expression is therefore zero, that is, every determinant in the transformed matrix of order greater than the rank of the original is zero. This shows that the elementary transformation does not increase the rank. If it diminished the rank, the inverse elementary transformation would increase it. Hence the theorem has been completely proved.

To determine the rank of a matrix, we apply elementary transformations as in the case of determinants, until at most one element in each row and column is different from zero. An application of transformation (ii), as modified for matrices, will subsequently make all non-zero elements $+1$. The rank is then the number of 1's.

Illustrative Example.

2	−3	4	5		0	−13	−2	−7
1	5	3	6		1	5	3	6
3	2	7	11		0	−13	−2	−7
1	−8	1	−1		0	−13	−2	−7

0	−13	−2	−7		0	−13	−2	−7
1	0	0	0		1	0	0	0
0	−13	−2	−7		0	0	0	0
0	−13	−2	−7		0	0	0	0

$$\begin{matrix} 0 & -13 & 0 & 0 \\ 1 & 0 & 0 & 0 \\ 0 & 0 & 0 & 0 \\ 0 & 0 & 0 & 0 \end{matrix} \qquad \begin{matrix} 0 & 1 & 0 & 0 \\ 1 & 0 & 0 & 0 \\ 0 & 0 & 0 & 0 \\ 0 & 0 & 0 & 0 \end{matrix}$$

Thus the rank is 2.

EXERCISES

Find the rank of each of the following matrices:

24.1. $\begin{matrix} 2 & -3 & 4 & -5 \\ -11 & 9 & 11 & -13 \\ -3 & 2 & 5 & -6 \end{matrix}$.

24.2. $\begin{matrix} 1 & 3 & 5 & 4 & 5 \\ -2 & 12 & 8 & 10 & 14 \\ 4 & -6 & 2 & -2 & -4 \\ 5 & -3 & 7 & 2 & 1 \end{matrix}$.

24.3. $\begin{matrix} 3 & -2 & 4 & 5 \\ 2 & -4 & 5 & 3 \\ 6 & 3 & 2 & 2 \\ 7 & 5 & 1 & 4 \end{matrix}$.

24.4. $\begin{matrix} 2 & -4 & 5 & 9 & 7 \\ 8 & 3 & 1 & 4 & 6 \\ 10 & -1 & 6 & 13 & 13 \end{matrix}$

24.5. $\begin{matrix} 0 & 1 & 1 & 1 \\ -1 & 0 & 1 & 2 \\ -1 & -1 & 0 & 1 \\ -1 & -2 & -1 & 0 \end{matrix}$.

24.6. $\begin{matrix} 1 & 2 & 3 \\ 3 & 2 & 1 \\ 4 & 1 & 5 \end{matrix}$.

24.7. $\begin{matrix} 0 & a & b & c & d \\ -a & 0 & e & f & g \\ -b & -e & 0 & h & k \\ -c & -f & -h & 0 & l \\ -d & -g & -k & -l & 0 \end{matrix}$.

Further reading on determinants and matrices will be found in A. A. Albert's, *Modern Algebra*, Chicago, 1937; M. Bôcher's *Introduction to Higher Algebra*, New York, 1921; G. Kowalewski's *Einführung in die Determinantentheorie*, Leipzig, 1909.

CHAPTER IV

SYSTEMS OF LINEAR EQUATIONS

25. *n* **Linear Equations in** *n* **Unknowns.**—Consider the *linear system*

$$(25.1) \qquad a_k^j x^k = b^j \qquad (j, k = 1, 2, \cdots, n),$$

where the superscripts are labels and not exponents and where we are using the summation convention of Sec. 18. It is proposed to determine x's satisfying[1] the system when the a's and b's are given.

If the equations are multiplied by the A_j^i of Sec. 16, there results

$$A_j^i a_k^j x^k = A_j^i b^j \qquad (i, j, k = 1, 2, \cdots, n).$$

By (20.2) the left member is $a\delta_k^i x^k$, which reduces to ax^i because $\delta_k^i = 0$, if $i \neq k$. Hence (25.1) imply

$$(25.2) \qquad ax^i = A_j^i b^j.$$

If $a \neq 0$, equations (25.1) imply

$$(25.3) \qquad x^i = A_j^i b^j / a.$$

Conversely, we can prove that (25.3) imply (25.1). In the first place, equations (25.3) imply (25.2). Multiplication of (25.2) by a_i^k gives

$$a a_i^k x^i = a_i^k A_j^i b^j = a\delta_j^k b^j = ab^k.$$

[1] That is, to find complex numbers which on being substituted for the indeterminates (Sec. 29) make the complex numbers, on the left of (25.1) equal to those on the right. When (25.1) is regarded in this light, the indeterminates are called unknowns.

Since $a \neq 0$, division by a shows that equations (25.3) imply (25.1).

THEOREM 25.1.—*A system of n linear equations in n unknowns with non-vanishing determinant has a unique solution.*

If we compare the right members of (25.2) with (20.2) in which $k = i$, we see that they are formed from determinant a by replacing the elements of the ith column by the b's. Formulas (25.3) constitute *Cramer's rule*:

The expression for each unknown is a fraction whose denominator is the determinant of the system and whose numerator is the result of replacing in that determinant the column corresponding to the unknown by the right members.

Illustrative Example.

$$3y + 2x - z = -3,$$
$$x + y + z = 2,$$
$$2z - x + y = 2.$$

First adopt a definite order for the unknowns, say x, y, z, and rewrite the equations accordingly

(25.4)
$$2x + 3y - z = -3,$$
$$x + y + z = 2,$$
$$-x + y + 2z = 2.$$

Next write the four determinants

$$\begin{vmatrix} 2 & 3 & -1 \\ 1 & 1 & 1 \\ -1 & 1 & 2 \end{vmatrix}, \begin{vmatrix} -3 & 3 & -1 \\ 2 & 1 & 1 \\ 2 & 1 & 2 \end{vmatrix}, \begin{vmatrix} 2 & -3 & -1 \\ 1 & 2 & 1 \\ -1 & 2 & 2 \end{vmatrix}, \begin{vmatrix} 2 & 3 & -3 \\ 1 & 1 & 2 \\ -1 & 1 & 2 \end{vmatrix},$$

the first of which is the determinant of the system and contains the coefficients in exactly their disposition in (25.4), the second of which is obtained from the first by replacing its first column by the right members of (25.4), etc. The reader should calculate the values of these determinants and find them to be

$$-9, \quad -9, \quad 9, \quad -18.$$

The solution, obtained by dividing the last three of these numbers by the first, is 1, -1, 2.

EXERCISES

Solve the following systems by Cramer's rule:

25.1. $\begin{aligned} 3x - 2y &= 5, \\ y + 2x &= 8. \end{aligned}$

25.2. $\begin{aligned} x + y - z &= 4, \\ y + z - x &= 0, \\ z + x - y &= 2. \end{aligned}$

25.3. $\begin{aligned} x + y + z &= 1, \\ ax + by + cz &= d, \\ a^2x + b^2y + c^2z &= d^2. \end{aligned}$

25.4. $\begin{aligned} 2x - 3y + 4z + 3t &= 7, \\ 3x + 2y - 6z + 4t &= -19, \\ 5x + y - z + 2t &= -2, \\ 2x - y + 2z - 2t &= 11. \end{aligned}$

26. Exceptional Cases.—Equations (25.1) do not represent the most general linear system, nor does Cramer's rule furnish a solution if the determinant is zero. A complete theory will presently be developed.

First, however, we wish to illustrate by graphical methods how the process of the preceding section fails when $a = 0$. To this end, consider the system of two equations ($n = 2$)

$$(26.1) \qquad \begin{aligned} ax + by &= c, \\ a'x + b'y &= c', \end{aligned}$$

where the coefficients are real and at least one coefficient on the left of each equation is not zero. Each of these is represented graphically (Chapter VI) by a straight line. If $bb' \neq 0$, the slopes of these lines are $-\dfrac{a}{b}$, $-\dfrac{a'}{b'}$. They are equal if and only if

$$(26.2) \qquad \begin{vmatrix} a & b \\ a' & b' \end{vmatrix} = 0,$$

that is, if and only if the determinant of the system vanishes. If $bb' = 0$, one of the lines is parallel to the y-axis, and in order that the two lines may have the same direction, both b and b' must be zero. Hence the condition (26.2) holds whenever the lines have the same direction. A solution is a point on both lines. Hence the unique solution found in Sec. 25 for this case $(n = 2)$ corresponds to intersecting lines, while in the exceptional case the lines are either (i) parallel or (ii) coincident. In (i) there is no point on both lines, that is, no solution, and in (ii) every point of the line gives a solution, that is, there are infinitely many solutions.

27. Homogeneous Systems.—The most general linear system is found by letting the indices in (25.1) have unequal ranges. To simplify matters, we first treat the case where all the b's are zero. Such a system is called *homogeneous*. It will be written

$$(27.1) \quad a_j^i x^j = 0 \qquad (i = 1, 2, \cdots, m; \ j = 1, 2, \cdots, q).$$

The a's form a matrix. Let its rank be n. A non-vanishing determinant of order n can be made to come from the first n rows simply by writing the equations in a different order, a process not affecting the system. Similarly, the non-zero determinant can be made to come from the first n columns by renumbering the unknowns, if necessary.

To simplify the notation, we let the first n unknowns be $x^1, \cdots, x^n$ and the others $y^1, \cdots, y^p$. The system can then be written

$$(27.2) \qquad\qquad a_j^i x^j + b_\beta^i y^\beta = 0,$$
$$(27.3) \qquad\qquad c_k^\alpha x^k + d_\beta^\alpha y^\beta = 0,$$
$$(i, j, k = 1, 2, \cdots, n; \alpha = n + 1, \cdots, m; \beta = 1, \cdots, p).$$

Since (27.2) is a system of n equations in the n unknown x's with non-vanishing determinant, Cramer's rule can be applied to its solution. An equivalent method of solution is to multiply by A_i^k and get

$$(27.4) \qquad\qquad a x^k = -A_i^k b_\beta^i y^\beta.$$

These results are known to satisfy only the first n of the equations, that is, (27.2). Their substitution in the others (27.3) gives

(27.5) $$(ad_\beta^\alpha - A_j^k b_\beta^j c_k^\alpha)y^\beta = 0.$$

Since the bordered determinant

$$\begin{vmatrix} a_j^i & b_\beta^i \\ c_j^\alpha & d_\beta^\alpha \end{vmatrix}$$

for fixed α, β is a determinant of order $n + 1$ from the matrix, it vanishes and (23.3) is applicable. Hence (27.5) is satisfied for arbitrary y's and we have

THEOREM 27.1.—*A linear homogeneous system of rank n has a solution expressing n of the unknowns as linear homogeneous functions of the others, which can be assigned arbitrary values.*

The solution just obtained is called a *general solution*, whereas that obtained by assigning values to some or all of the arbitrary unknowns is called a *particular solution*.

Illustrative Example.

$$2x + 3y - 4z + 5t = 0,$$
$$y - 2z + x + 4t = 0,$$
$$3x + 4y - 6z + 9t = 0,$$
$$x + 2y - 2z + t = 0.$$

Let the order x, y, z, t be adopted for the unknowns. The rank is readily found to be 2. The first two equations can be written as

$$2x + 3y = 4z - 5t,$$
$$x + y = 2z - 4t,$$

which have determinant -1. The solution by Cramer's rule is given by

$$\begin{vmatrix} 2 & 3 \\ 1 & 1 \end{vmatrix}, \qquad \begin{vmatrix} 4z - 5t & 3 \\ 2z - 4t & 1 \end{vmatrix}, \qquad \begin{vmatrix} 2 & 4z - 5t \\ 1 & 2z - 4t \end{vmatrix},$$

or

$$x = 2z - 7t, \qquad y = 3t.$$

Substitution of these values in the last two equations gives identities, as the theory predicts.

The solution can, of course, be given other forms. By solving for other pairs, we get

$$x = -\tfrac{7}{3}y + 2z, \qquad t = \tfrac{1}{3}y;$$
$$y = 3t, \qquad\qquad z = \tfrac{1}{2}x + \tfrac{7}{2}t;$$
$$y = -\tfrac{3}{7}x + \tfrac{6}{7}z, \qquad t = -\tfrac{1}{7}x + \tfrac{2}{7}z;$$
$$z = \tfrac{1}{2}x + \tfrac{7}{6}y, \qquad t = \tfrac{1}{3}y.$$

The system, however, cannot be solved for the pair x, z because every determinant of order two formed from the first and third columns is zero. This is tantamount to saying that the unknowns y and t cannot be arbitrary. In fact, they are related by $y = 3t$.

It is often (for example, in the following section) important to know whether a linear homogeneous system of equations has a solution in which a given set of the unknowns can be assigned arbitrary values. This question is answered by

THEOREM 27.2.—*A linear homogeneous system of equations has a solution in which a given set of the unknowns has arbitrary values if and only if deleting from the matrix the columns corresponding to those unknowns leaves the rank unaltered.*

The sufficiency of the condition is given by Theorem 27.1. If the rank is n when the given unknowns are disregarded, the system can be solved for n of the other unknowns and the given unknowns appear as arbitrary quantities in the solution.

The condition is necessary. If the rank were diminished by disregarding the given unknowns, then for every solution of the system by the method developed above at least one of the given unknowns would appear as an x and no solution would contain them all as arbitrary unknowns (or *parameters*, as they are sometimes called).

Thus in the illustrative example of this section, if we omit the second and fourth columns, which correspond to y, t, respectively, the rank becomes 1, so that there is no solution in which y, t are arbitrary parameters. On the other hand, the omission of any other pair of columns leaves the rank 2, so that there is a solution with any other pair of unknowns arbitrary.

Any homogeneous system is obviously satisfied by making all the unknowns zero. This solution is called the *trivial* solution. Any other, that is, any solution in which at least one unknown is not zero, is called *non-trivial*.

If x^i, y^α is a solution of a homogeneous system, so also is λx^i, λy^α obtained by multiplying its values by the arbitrary constant λ. If any x^i or y^α is not zero, it can accordingly be made arbitrary. If the rank of a system is equal to the number of unknowns, there are no arbitrary unknowns and consequently there is only the trivial solution. This result also readily follows from the process of solution. If, on the other hand, the rank is less than the number of unknowns, there is at least one arbitrary unknown, which can be made different from zero to give a non-trivial solution.

THEOREM 27.3.—*A homogeneous linear system has a non-trivial solution if and only if its rank is less than the number of unknowns.*

We close this section with several properties of matrices, whose proof the theory developed above renders easy.

Suppose the rank of (27.2), (27.3) is not known to be n. Suppose, however, that the determinant a is not zero and that every determinant of order $n + 1$ containing it is zero. Then the solution of (27.2) satisfies (27.3) as before. We can prove the rank is n. For, if the rank were greater than n, the omission of the last p columns would diminish the rank, and by Theorem 27.2 the system could not have a solution in which y^1, y^2, $\cdots$, y^p are arbitrary. Hence we have

THEOREM 27.4.—*The rank of a matrix is n if and only if it contains a non-zero determinant D of order n and every determinant of order $n + 1$ which is in the matrix and contains D is zero.*

This materially diminishes the labor of expressing that a matrix has a given rank.

Suppose a non-zero determinant D of order r is contained in a matrix of rank n. Then $r \leq n$. If every determinant of order $r + 1$ which is in the matrix and contains D is zero, then $r = n$. If $r < n$, some determinant D' of order $r + 1$ containing D must be different from zero. Continuing this argument, we conclude that D is contained in a non-zero determinant of order n.

THEOREM 27.5.—*Every non-zero determinant in a matrix of rank n is contained in at least one non-zero determinant of order n in the matrix.*

If a system of linear homogeneous equations has a non-trivial solution, its matrix is said to be *linearly dependent by columns*. This means that it is possible to associate with each column a multiplier such that at least one multiplier is not zero and such that the result of multiplying the columns by the corresponding multipliers and adding is zero. A similar definition applies to *linear dependence by rows*. From Theorem 27.3 we have

THEOREM 27.6.—*A matrix is linearly dependent by rows if and only if its rank is less than the number of rows, and this statement remains true if the word "rows" is replaced by "columns."*

Each left member of system (27.1) is called a *linear form* in the indeterminates x. Let us write

$$v^i = a^i_j x^j.$$

The *rank* of the set of forms is that of the matrix a^i_j. The set of forms v is called *linearly dependent* if the system obtained by equating to zero the coefficients of x^j in

$$\lambda_i v^i$$

has a non-trivial solution. The matrix of the system in the unknowns λ_i is obviously the *transpose* (Sec. 14) of a^i_j. Hence we have

THEOREM 27.7.—*A set of linear forms is linearly dependent if and only if their rank is less than their number.*

This result will be supplemented at the end of the next section.

EXERCISES

27.1–27.6. Write the systems of linear homogeneous equations having the matrices of Exercises 24.1–24.6, and solve them.

27.7. Prove Theorem 27.3 by means of Cramer's rule.

27.8. Use Theorem 27.3 to eliminate r_3, r_4, r_5 among equations (3.5).

27.9. Prove that the result of eliminating the x's among the equations

$$a^i_j x^i = b^i \qquad (i = 1, 2, \cdots, n; j = 1, 2, \cdots, n+1)$$

is the determinant of the augmented matrix (Sec. 28) equated to zero.

27.10. Prove that a square matrix linearly dependent by rows is linearly dependent by columns, and conversely.

28. Non-homogeneous Linear Systems.—The type to be studied here is (27.1) with its right members replaced by symbols not necessarily zero:

$$(28.1) \quad a^i_j x^j = b^i \qquad (i = 1, 2, \cdots, m; j = 1, 2, \cdots, q).$$

Its matrix is the matrix of the a's. To study the system we introduce an additional unknown z and write

(28.2) $a^i_j x^j + b^i z = 0.$

The matrix of this system is that of (28.1) with an additional column of b's. It is called the *augmented matrix* of (28.1).

Any solution of the homogeneous system (28.2) which has $z = -1$ will give a solution of the non-homogeneous system (28.1). Now (28.2) has a solution with $z = -1$ if and only if it has a solution with z arbitrary. Consequently, Theorem 27.2 gives the condition for the consistency of (28.1), namely,

THEOREM 28.1.—*A non-homogeneous system has a solution if and only if its matrix and its augmented matrix have the same rank.*

We shall close the discussion of non-homogeneous systems with the above criterion. As we have already seen, their actual solution can be accomplished by solving the corresponding homogeneous system (28.2). We shall now apply the theory to a brief study of linear dependence of forms.

If the forms v^k ($k = 1, 2, \cdots, l$) in the indeterminates x^i ($i = 1, 2, \cdots, n$) have rank r, there is a subset of r forms whose rank is also r. A renumbering of the forms, if necessary, will always make $v^1, \cdots, v^r$ of rank r. If v is any form of the set, then $v^1, \cdots, v^r, v$ is a linearly dependent set and we wish to show that λ's can be determined to make

(28.3) $v = \lambda_\alpha v^\alpha$ $(\alpha = 1, 2, \cdots, r)$

an identity. If

$$v = b_i x^i, \qquad v^\alpha = a^\alpha_i x^i,$$

equating the coefficients of x^i in (28.3) gives

(28.4) $a^\alpha_i \lambda_\alpha = b_i.$

The rank of the matrix of this non-homogeneous system is r because $v^1, \cdots, v^r$ are of rank r. The augmented matrix is the matrix of $v^1, \cdots, v^r, v$ and by use of Theorem 27.7 its rank is seen to be r. Hence (28.4) have a solution by Theorem 28.1.

Because of (28.3) the form v is said to be *linearly dependent* on $v^1, \cdots, v^r$, and we have

THEOREM 28.2.—*From a set of linear forms we can find a subset whose rank is that of the whole set and on which the whole set is linearly dependent.*

To illustrate the theory, we return to the straight lines (26.1). Let r be the rank of the system and R that of the augmented system. There are only three cases since $r \leqq R$.

(i) $r = R = 2$. There is a unique solution and the lines intersect.

(ii) $r = 1, R = 2$. There is no solution and the lines are parallel.

(iii) $r = R = 1$. There is an infinity of solutions with either x or y arbitrary and the lines are coincident.

Consider also the three planes in space given by

$$(28.5) \quad \begin{aligned} ax + by + cz &= d, \\ a'x + b'y + c'z &= d', \\ a''x + b''y + c''z &= d''. \end{aligned}$$

At least one coefficient on the left of each equation is supposed different from zero, since we wish each equation actually to represent a plane.

(i) $r = R = 3$. Unique point of intersection.

(ii) $r = 2, R = 3$. Two of the planes intersect in a line parallel to the third.

(iii) $r = R = 2$. Two of the planes intersect in a line through which the third passes. The third may be coincident with one of the others.

(iv) $r = 1$, $R = 2$.   Three parallel planes.[1]

(v) $r = 1$, $R = 2$.   Two planes coincident and parallel to the third.[1]

(vi) $r = R = 1$.   Three coincident planes.

EXERCISES

28.1–28.6. Form the non-homogeneous linear systems having the matrices of Exercises 24.1–24.6 for augmented matrices, the last column corresponding to the right members.   Solve the resulting systems.   (In cases of inconsistency, the answer to the problem is merely a statement that the system has no solution.)

28.7. Prove that if r, R respectively represent the ranks of the matrix and the augmented matrix of a non-homogeneous system, then $r = R$ or $r = R - 1$.

28.8. Associate an indeterminate with each column of the matrices in Sec. 24.   Each row then gives a linear form.   Express each set of linear forms in terms of a subset, that is, find equations like (28.3).

28.9. Verify directly that the linear forms in the left members of (27.3) are linearly dependent on those of (27.2).

28.10. Let (a, b) be a point in the plane.   What geometric figure is formed by all the points linearly dependent on (a, b), that is, by all points (x, y) for which the matrix

$$\begin{matrix} a & b \\ x & y \end{matrix}$$

is linearly dependent?

28.11. Generalize Exercise 28.10 to three dimensions.

28.12. Write $x = (x^1, \cdots, x^n)$, $y = (y^1, \cdots, y^n)$ and define $x + y$ as $(x^1 + y^1, \cdots, x^n + y^n)$ and λx as $(\lambda x^1, \cdots, \lambda x^n)$.   Prove that if x, y are solutions of a linear homogeneous system in n unknowns, then $x + y$, $x - y$ and $\lambda x + \mu y$, where λ, μ are any constants, are also solutions.

28.13. If a linear homogeneous system in n unknowns has rank r, it has $n - r$ linearly independent solutions x^i_j, where i denotes the unknown and j the solution.   A set of solutions of rank $n - r$ is called a *fundamental set*.   Prove that every solution of the system is linearly dependent on any fundamental set.

---

[1] Case (iv) can be distinguished from (v) by the circumstance that in (iv) every pair of equations has augmented matrix of rank 2, whereas in (v) a pair of equations has augmented matrix of rank 1.

28.14. Show that a fundamental set of solutions is obtained by giving the arbitrary unknowns in the solutions of Sec. 27 successively the values

$$
\begin{array}{cccc}
1 & 0 & \cdots & 0 \\
0 & 1 & \cdots & 0 \\
\cdot\cdot\cdot & \cdot\cdot\cdot & \cdot\cdot\cdot & \cdot\cdot\cdot \\
0 & 0 & \cdots & 1.
\end{array}
$$

28.15. Interpret the result of Exercise 28.13 geometrically in the two cases where the system is

(i) $ax + by = 0$;   (ii) $ax + by + cz = 0$.

28.16. Prove that a non-homogeneous system can always be solved by replacing the right members by zero, solving the homogeneous system so obtained, and finally adding any particular solution of the original system.

28.17. Apply Theorem 28.1 to the case treated in Sec. 25.

28.18. Augment the matrix M of a linear homogeneous system by placing below it a square matrix M' with the same number of columns and with elements δ_j^i. Introduce zeros into M as in Sec. 24 by transforming the columns alone (that is, apply (iii), p. 28, to columns, but not to rows) in the augmented matrix. Prove that when the transform of M contains a column of zeros, the values in the same column of the transform of M' give a solution of the system, and show how to construct a general solution in this manner. (*Cf.* H. T. Burgess, American Mathematical Monthly, vol. 25 (1918), pp. 441–444.) A preliminary determination of the rank is unnecessary when this method is applied.

Linear systems are treated also in Bôcher's *Higher Algebra* and Kowalewski's *Determinantentheorie* previously cited.

CHAPTER V

POLYNOMIALS IN A SINGLE INDETERMINATE

29. Definitions.—A symbol x which is not a complex number is called an *indeterminate* if we agree that it can be combined with complex numbers by operations $+$, $-$, $\times$, $\div$ which satisfy the laws given in Chapter I.

To emphasize the difference between them and indeterminates complex numbers will be called *constants*.

We now use x^n to denote $xx \cdots x$ to n factors.

If a is a complex number and m is a non-negative integer, ax^m is a *monomial*, whose *coefficient* is a, and whose degree is m if $a \neq 0$. The monomial 0 has no degree.

A *polynomial* is a sum of a finite number of monomials. It can be written

$$(29.1) \qquad f(x) = a_0 x^m + a_1 x^{m-1} + \cdots + a_{m-1} x + a_m.$$

Note that the sum of subscript and superscript in each term is m. The coefficient a_0 is called the *initial* of the polynomial.[1] If $a_0 \neq 0$, the *degree* of the polynomial is m. The monomial $a_0 x^m$ is the *leader*.

The nature of a polynomial, we shall see, depends essentially upon the set from which the coefficients a_i are taken, that is, whether they all belong to $\mathcal{J}$, $\mathcal{R}$, $\mathcal{X}$, or $\mathbf{3}$ is often of importance. The set of all polynomials in x with coefficients from a ring R will be denoted by $R[x]$. Thus, saying f belongs to $\mathcal{J}[x]$ means that it is a polynomial in the indeterminate x with integers for coefficients.

---

[1] The useful name "initial" was apparently first employed by J. F. Ritt, *Differential Equations from the Algebraic Standpoint*, New York, 1932.

The reader should prove that $R[x]$ is a *ring*, the so-called *polynomial ring* associated with the ring R.

30. Division of Polynomials.—Consider a polynomial

$$(30.1) \quad g(x) = b_0x^n + b_1x^{n-1} + \cdots + b_{n-1}x + b_n$$

in addition to (29.1). We may suppose $a_0b_0 \neq 0$ and $m \geqq n$.
The polynomial

$$(30.2) \qquad\qquad f_1 = b_0f - a_0x^{m-n}g$$

has degree at most $m - 1$ because the terms of degree m cancel. Let it be written with leader $a_{10}x^{m-1}$ (a_{10} may be zero). If $m - 1 \geqq n$, form

$$(30.3) \qquad\qquad f_2 = b_0f_1 - a_{10}x^{m-n-1}g.$$

Continuing, we finally get an f_l of degree less than n or an $f_l = 0$. (By supplying a zero coefficient, when necessary, we have made the highest exponent diminish by one each time.) By combining the expressions for the f_i we get

$$(30.4) \qquad\qquad b_0^{m-n+1}f = Qg + R,$$

where Q and R are polynomials. The degree of Q is $m - n$ and R has degree less than n or is zero.

Since the only operations involved are $+$, $-$, $\times$, the Q, R will have coefficients in any ring from which the coefficients of f, g are taken. Thus if the coefficients of f, g are integers, so also are those of Q, R.

If $b_0 = 1$ in (30.4), the polynomials Q, R are, respectively, the quotient and remainder when f is divided by g. Even when $b_0 \neq 1$, they are the quotient and remainder when $b_0^{m-n+1}f$ is divided by g; and the quotient and remainder for $f \div g$ are easily deduced from them. The introduction of b_0^{m-n+1} simply avoids fractions in the work. A lower (even the zero-th) power of b_0 may suffice in particular cases, but there is no harm in introducing too high a power.

Let us illustrate with the polynomials

$$f = 3x^4 + 2x^3 - x^2 + x + 5, \qquad g = 2x^2 - x + 1.$$

Here $m - n + 1 = 3$. Hence we take $8f$ for the dividend and the work is arranged below.

$$
\begin{array}{l|l}
24x^4 + 16x^3 - 8x^2 + 8x + 40 & 2x^2 - x + 1 \\
\underline{24x^4 - 12x^3 + 12x^2} & 12x^2 + 14x - 3 \\
\quad + 28x^3 - 20x^2 + 8x \\
\quad \underline{28x^3 - 14x^2 + 14x} \\
\qquad - 6x^2 - 6x + 40 \\
\qquad \underline{- 6x^2 + 3x - 3} \\
\qquad\qquad - 9x + 43
\end{array}
$$

Thus $Q = 12x^2 + 14x - 3$, $R = -9x + 43$, and the quotient and remainder for $f \div g$ are $\frac{1}{8}Q$, $\frac{1}{8}R$.

31. Synthetic Division.—Let us attempt to eliminate all unnecessary steps in the preceding example. In the first place, it is not necessary to write the products of the leader of the divisor by the quotient because they always cancel. Secondly, if we change the sign of all terms of the divisor, except the first, subtraction can be replaced by addition. Finally, as the terms of the polynomials are written according to decreasing exponent, the powers of x can be omitted. Thus we get the following arrangement.

$$
\begin{array}{l|l}
24 \quad +16 \quad - 8 \quad + 8 \quad +40 & 2 \quad +1 \quad -1 \\
\qquad +12 \quad -12 \\
\qquad\qquad +14 \quad -14 \\
\qquad\qquad\qquad - 3 \quad + 3 \\
\hline
\quad 12 \quad +14 \quad - 3 \;\big|\; - 9 \quad +43
\end{array}
$$

The first number on the last line is obtained by dividing 24 by the initial of the divisor, 2. The other two coefficients in the divisor are then multiplied by 12 and the results placed as indicated. The second column is then added and the sum divided by 2 to give 14, which is the second coefficient in the quotient. The 14 is then multiplied by the last two terms of the divisor, and the third column is added and divided by 2 to give the third coefficient of the quotient, namely, -3. This is then multiplied by the last two terms of the divisor. The termination of the division is indicated by the 3's appearing under the 40, that is, just to the left of the vertical line. The remaining columns are then totaled (*without* division by 2) to give the remainder.

The number of rows for which space must be left equals the number of terms in the quotient. It is therefore $m - n + 1$.

In applying this shortened or *synthetic* division, we must be careful to arrange the polynomials in descending powers of x and to supply any missing terms with zero coefficients. Thus the division of $x^5 - 1$ by $x - 1$ is

$$
\begin{array}{cccccc|cc}
1 & +0 & +0 & +0 & +0 & -1 & 1 & +1 \\
  & +1 &   &   &   &   &   &   \\
  &   & +1 &   &   &   &   &   \\
  &   &   & +1 &   &   &   &   \\
  &   &   &   & +1 &   &   &   \\
  &   &   &   &   & +1 &   &   \\
\hline
1 & +1 & +1 & +1 & +1 & +0 &   &
\end{array}
$$

Since the remainder is zero, f is divisible by g.

The work can be further condensed, in the case of the last example, as shown below.

$$
\begin{array}{cccccc|c}
1 & +0 & +0 & +0 & +0 & -1 & +1 \\
  & +1 & +1 & +1 & +1 & +1 & \\
\hline
1 & +1 & +1 & +1 & +1 & +0 &
\end{array}
$$

Thus the initial of the divisor is not written and there is a vertical condensation as well. Such condensation is always possible and customary when the divisor is of the form $x + a$.

EXERCISES

Apply synthetic division to the following:

31.1. $\dfrac{x^3 + 3x + 1}{2x + 1}$.

31.2. $\dfrac{3x^4 + 2x^2 - 3x + 2}{3x^2 + 2x - 1}$.

31.3. $\dfrac{2x^5 - 3x^4 + 4x^3 - x^2 - x + 2}{x^3 + x + 1}$.

31.4. $\dfrac{6x^5 + 19x^4 + 4x^3 - 13x^2 + 10x - 2}{2x^2 + 3x - 1}$.

31.5. $\dfrac{15x^4 + 14x^3 - 21x^2 + 2}{5x^2 - 2x - 1}$.

31.6. $\dfrac{3x^3 + 4x^2 - x + 1}{2x^2 - x + 1}$.

32. The Remainder and Factor Theorems.—If the divisor g is of the form $x - a$, formula (30.4) becomes

$$(32.1) \qquad f(x) = (x - a)Q(x) + R,$$

where R is a constant, since its highest exponent does not exceed $n - 1 = 0$.

By substituting $x = a$ we find

$$f(a) = R,$$

a result which will be stated as

REMAINDER THEOREM 32.1.—*The remainder when $f(x)$ is divided by $x - a$ is the same as the result of substituting a for x in $f(x)$.*

The synthetic division of Sec. 31 therefore gives a ready means of calculating $f(a)$. Note that *the sign of the synthetic divisor is the* same *as that of the number substituted.*

A corollary is the

FACTOR THEOREM 32.2.—*A polynomial $f(x)$ vanishes for $x = a$ if and only if it is divisible by $x - a$.*

The number a is called a *root* of the polynomial $f(x)$ and of the equation $f(x) = 0$ if $f(a) = 0$.

From the factor theorem follows the important result

THEOREM 32.3.—*The number of roots possessed by a polynomial does not exceed its degree.*

The theorem is true for degree 1. If a polynomial f of degree n has a root a, then $f = (x - a)Q$, where Q is of degree $n - 1$ because the coefficient of x^{n-1} in it is the same as the initial of f. If the theorem is assumed for all polynomials of degree not exceeding $n - 1$, it immediately follows for all polynomials of degree n, and the result is true by induction for all values of n.

33. Derivatives.—If $f(x)$ is a polynomial of degree n, then $f(x + h)$, the result of replacing x by $x + h$, is also a polynomial of degree n. It can be written as a polynomial in either x or h. Let it be written as a polynomial in h. Its coefficients are then polynomials in x. We write

$$(33.1)\quad f(x + h) = f^{(0)}(x) + hf'(x) + \frac{h^2}{2!}f''(x)$$
$$+ \cdots + \frac{h^n}{n!}f^{(n)}(x).$$

The polynomial $f^{(k)}(x)$ is called the kth *derivative* of $f(x)$, if k does not exceed the degree n; if $k > n$ or if the polynomial is 0, the derivative is defined to be zero. In particular, by making $h = 0$ we infer $f^{(0)}(x) = f(x)$.

Multiplication of (33.1) by the constant c and addition of (33.1) to a similar equation for a second polynomial $g(x)$ give the important laws

$$(33.2)\qquad (cf)^{(k)} = cf^{(k)}, \qquad (f + g)^{(k)} = f^{(k)} + g^{(k)}.$$

The same formulas are easily seen to hold when k exceeds the degree of f or g. Hence, *the derivative of a constant times a polynomial is the constant times the derivative of the polynomial,* and *the derivative of a sum is the sum of the derivatives.* We shall be able to find the derivatives of any polynomial if we know the derivatives of x^m. By using the definition, the non-zero derivatives are found from the coefficients of the successive powers of h in $(x + h)^m$ to be

$$(33.3) \quad x^m, \quad mx^{m-1}, \quad m(m-1)x^{m-2}, \quad \cdots, \quad m!.$$

All the derivatives of any constant are readily seen to be zero.

The first derivative can be obtained from the zero-th by *multiplying by the exponent of x and then diminishing the exponent by* 1. This same process applied to any member of the sequence (33.3) gives the following member. We therefore have *for powers of x*

$$(33.4) \quad [f^{(k-1)}]' = f^{(k)},$$

and (33.2) shows that the same result holds *for any polynomial.*

The derivatives of $(x + a)^m$, in similar fashion, are

$$(33.5) \quad (x + a)^m, \quad m(x + a)^{m-1}, \quad \cdots.$$

Finally, we need the result

$$(33.6) \quad (fg)' = fg' + f'g.$$

The left member is the coefficient of h in the product

$$f(x + h)g(x + h).$$

By (33.1) the product is written

$$[f(x) + hf'(x) + \cdots][g(x) + hg'(x) + \cdots],$$

and the coefficient in question is readily seen to be the right member of (33.6).

The reader will identify the derivatives just discussed with those defined in the differential calculus in another manner.

EXERCISES

Find the derivatives of the following polynomials:
33.1. $x^2 + x + 1$.
33.2. $2x^5 + 4x^3 - 5x + 4$.
33.3. $(x - 1)^5$.

34. Multiple Roots.—If a is a root of $f(x) = 0$, by the factor theorem $f(x)$ is divisible by $x - a$. It may be divisible by a higher power of $x - a$ than the first. Let k be the exponent of the highest power of $x - a$ dividing $f(x)$. By the factor theorem

$$(34.1) \qquad f(x) = (x - a)^k \varphi(x), \qquad \varphi(a) \neq 0.$$

The root a is said to have *multiplicity k*. Roots of multiplicity 1, 2, 3, k are respectively called *simple, double, triple, k-fold*. If the multiplicity is greater than one, the root is called *multiple*. In speaking of the number of the roots, a k-fold root will always be counted as k roots, unless something is said to the contrary.

From (34.1) we get

$$(34.2) \qquad f'(x) = k(x - a)^{k-1} \varphi(x) + (x - a)^k \varphi'(x).$$

Hence a is a root of $f'(x)$ of multiplicity at least $k - 1$. On the other hand, if $(x - a)^k$ were a divisor of $f'(x)$, $(x - a)^k$ would have to be a divisor of the first term of the right member in (34.2) and $(x - a)$ would have to be a divisor of $\varphi(x)$, contrary to hypothesis. Hence

THEOREM 34.1.—*If $f(x)$ has a root of multiplicity k then $f'(x)$ has that root with multiplicity $k - 1$.*

This means, of course, that if $k = 1$ for the root $x = a$, $f'(x)$ does not have a as a root.

35. Highest Common Factor of Two Polynomials.—If r_1 and r_2 are two polynomials and the degree of r_1 is not less than that of r_2, we may divide r_1 by r_2 and get a remainder r_3 which is either zero or has degree less than that of r_2. We thus construct, much as in the case of Euclid's algorithm (Sec. 3) for integers, a sequence of polynomials of decreasing degree. The process stops when a polynomial of degree zero, that is, a nonzero constant, or when the polynomial zero is encountered. In the first case, any factor common to r_1 and r_2 will have to be a divisor of a non-zero constant and hence will be a constant; the polynomials are called *relatively prime*. If the last member of the sequence is zero, as in the case of the integers the polynomial r_l is the *highest common factor*.

The computation of the highest common factor is readily accomplished by synthetic division.

It should be noted that when the coefficients are integers and x is made equal to an integer, the polynomials become integers. The polynomial which is their highest common factor also becomes an integer, but although it is necessarily a common factor of the integers to which the polynomials reduce, it may not be their *highest* common factor.

Illustrative Example.—Find the highest common factor of

$$2x^4 - 5x^3 + 6x^2 - 4x + 1, \qquad 2x^4 - x^3 - 2x + 1.$$

The work is arranged as follows.

$$
\begin{array}{rrrrr|rrrrr}
4 & -10 & +12 & -8 & +2 & 2 & +1 & +0 & +2 & -1 \\
& +2 & +0 & +4 & -2 & & & & & \\
\hline
2 \ | & -8 & +12 & -4 & +0 & & & & & \\
16 & -8 & +0 & -16 & +8 & 2 & +3 & -1 & & \\
& +24 & -8 & & & & & & & \\
& & +24 & -8 & & & & & & \\
& & & +24 & -8 & & & & & \\
\hline
8 & +8 & +8 \ | & 0 & 0 & & & & &
\end{array}
$$

Hence the highest common factor is $2x^2 - 3x + 1$, because it is the last non-zero r in the sequence (3.1).

The first remainder is to be used as the second divisor. It, however, has the factor $-4x$, which can be removed because of the following obvious principle:

The removal of a factor from an r in sequence (3.1) does not alter the highest common factor, provided the factor does not divide at least one member of the sequence.

Hence $2x^2 - 3x + 1$ can be used for the second divisor rather than $-8x^3 + 12x^2 - 4x$.

EXERCISES

Find the highest common factor of the following pairs of polynomials:

35.1. $x^5 + 2x^2 - 4x + 1$, $x^3 - 2x^2 - 2x + 3$.

35.2. $x^6 - 2x^4 - 2x^3 - 2x^2 - 3x - 2$, $x^3 - 4x^2 + x + 6$.

35.3. $2x^3 + x^2 + 3x - 1$, $x^2 + x + 1$.

35.4. $2x^3 + x^2 + 2x + 1$, $2x^5 + x^4 + 2x + 1$.

35.5. $x^4 + x^3 + 2x^2 + 3x + 1$, $x^4 - x^3 + 2x^2 - x - 1$.

36. Elimination of Multiple Roots.

By the results of Sec. 34 if $f(x)$ has a k-fold root, the highest common factor $g(x)$ of f and f' has that root as a $(k - 1)$-fold root. Hence f/g will have that root as a simple root.

Accordingly, by finding the highest common factor of f and f' and removing it from f by division, we get a polynomial having the same roots as f but with no multiple roots. Its determination requires only the operations $+$, $-$, $\times$.

EXERCISES

The following polynomials have double roots.   Find them.

36.1. $2x^4 - x^3 - 5x^2 + 5x - 1$.

36.2. $x^4 - 2x^3 - 7x^2 + 20x - 12$.

36.3. $x^4 + 5x^3 + 9x^2 + 8x + 4$.

For each of the following polynomials, find a polynomial having the same roots as simple roots:

36.4. $x^4 + 3x^3 + 4x^2 + 3x + 1$.

36.5. $x^4 + 3x^3 + 2x^2 + 4x + 8$.

36.6. $x^4 - 2x^3 + 3x^2 - 2x + 1$.

36.7. Find by the method of Sec. 34 the condition that $ax^2 + bx + c$ have equal roots.

37. Reducibility.

If a polynomial f of the ring $R[x]$ can be written as the product of two polynomials g, h of lower degree belonging to $R[x]$, then f is said to be *reducible in R*; otherwise it is *irreducible in R*. This means, for example, that if a polynomial with integral coefficients is the product of two like polynomials, neither of which is of degree zero, it is reducible in the ring of integers. Similarly, for the rational, real, and complex rings. It will ultimately be clear (Sec. 60) that every polynomial with complex coefficients and with degree greater than one is reducible in the complex field.

Note that reducibility is a relative term. Thus $x^2 - 2$ is irreducible in the ring of integers and in the rational field, but it is reducible in the field of reals.

An equation is reducible or irreducible in a field according as its left number is reducible or irreducible in that field.

A result useful in subsequent chapters is

Theorem 37.1.—*If f, g have coefficients in a field $\mathfrak{F}$, if g is irreducible in $\mathfrak{F}$ and if f, g have a root in common, then f is divisible by g and the coefficients of the quotient are in $\mathfrak{F}$.*

Since *f*, *g* have a common root, they have a non-constant common factor. The highest common factor is found by rational operations. If it were of lower degree than *g*, the polynomial *g* would be reducible in $\mathfrak{F}$.

38. Gauss' Lemma.—A polynomial in $\mathfrak{I}[x]$ whose coefficients have unity for highest common factor is called a *unit polynomial* (with respect to $\mathfrak{I}$).

A result of importance in questions of reducibility is

Theorem 38.1.—*A product of two polynomials in $\mathfrak{I}[x]$ is a unit polynomial if and only if its factors are unit polynomials.*

If $f = gh$, it is clear that the highest common factor of the coefficients of *g* is a factor of all the coefficients of *f*. Hence half of the theorem is rather obvious. The other half, known as Gauss' lemma, will now be proved.

It is convenient to modify the notation of Sec. 29 for polynomials and to write

$$f = a_0 + \cdots + a_m x^m, \qquad g = b_0 + \cdots + b_n x^n,$$
$$h = c_0 + \cdots + c_q x^q.$$

If the polynomials f, g, h are combined by ring operations, this notation makes the *weight*, that is, the sum of the subscripts on the coefficients in any term, equal to the degree of that term in x. Thus, if $f = gh$,

$$(38.1) \qquad a_{r+s} = b_r c_s + b_{r-1} c_{s+1} + b_{r+1} c_{s-1} + \cdots,$$

where all terms are of weight $r + s$.

Corresponding to any prime p, there exist r, s such that

$$b_0 \equiv b_1 \equiv \cdots \equiv b_{r-1} \equiv c_0 \equiv c_1 \equiv \cdots \equiv c_{s-1} \equiv 0,$$
$$b_r \not\equiv 0, \qquad c_s \not\equiv 0 \qquad (\text{mod } p),$$

that is, b_r is the first coefficient of g not divisible by p. It exists because g is a unit polynomial. Similarly for c_s. The other terms written in (38.1) are then divisible by p because b_{r-1}, c_{s-1} are. The same holds for the unwritten terms. Hence $a_{r+s} \equiv b_r c_s$ (mod p), and since p divides neither b_r nor c_s, it does not divide a_{r+s} (Theorem 3.3). Corresponding to any prime p there is accordingly at least one coefficient in the product which it does not divide. Hence the coefficients of the product are relatively prime.

39. Reducibility in the Rational Field.—For the ring of integers, the question of reducibility can be settled by a finite number of trials. Thus, to find whether $ax^2 + bx + c$ is reducible, we write

$$ax^2 + bx + c = (\alpha x + \beta)(\gamma x + \delta),$$

whence on performing the indicated multiplication we get

$$\alpha \gamma = a, \qquad \alpha \delta + \beta \gamma = b, \qquad \beta \delta = c.$$

Since the integers a, c can be written as the product of two integers in only a finite number of ways, we substitute in the second condition all values of α, β, γ, δ, satisfying the first and third. If no set of values satisfies, the polynomial is irreducible in the ring of integers. This is, essentially, the method given in elementary algebra for solving a quadratic equation "by factoring."

For polynomials of higher degree, this method, although it has been systematized by Kronecker,[1] is excessively tedious. Hence it is convenient to devise tests applicable to special classes of polynomials. One of these which we shall find useful is given in the next section.

The question of reducibility for a polynomial in the rational field is easily reduced to that for an *associated polynomial* in the ring of integers. Let $f = gh$ be a polynomial reducible in the rational field. We may write

$$f = \frac{c_1}{c_2}F, \qquad g = \frac{d_1}{d_2}G, \qquad h = \frac{e_1}{e_2}H,$$

where c_1, c_2, d_1, d_2, e_1, e_2 are positive integers and F, G, H are unit polynomials. Then

$$c_1 d_2 e_2 F = c_2 d_1 e_1 GH.$$

Any prime factor of $c_2 d_1 e_1$ divides all the coefficients on the left. It must therefore divide their highest common factor, which is $c_1 d_2 e_2$, since F is a unit polynomial. If the common prime factor is removed, the argument can be repeated, so that $c_1 d_2 e_2$ is seen to be divisible by $c_2 d_1 e_1$. Since GH is also a unit polynomial, $c_2 d_1 e_1$ is divisible by $c_1 d_2 e_2$. Therefore $c_1 d_2 e_2 = c_2 d_1 e_1$ and $F = GH$. Thus, f (*and hence the equation $f = 0$) is reducible in the rational field only if F is reducible in the ring of integers.* The converse is obvious.

[1] B. L. van der Waerden, *Moderne Algebra*, vol. 1, p. 82.

If in the preceding discussion f, g are unit polynomials, that is, if $c_1 = c_2$, $d_1 = d_2$, the argument given above shows that $e_1 = e_2$, that is,

THEOREM 39.1.—*If a unit polynomial is divisible by another unit polynomial, the quotient has integral coefficients and is a unit polynomial.*

40. Eisenstein's theorem is

THEOREM 40.1.—*If the initial of a polynomial is not divisible by a prime p, if all the other coefficients are divisible by p, and if the constant term is not divisible by p^2, the polynomial is irreducible.*

The phraseology of the theorem implies that reducibility with respect to the ring of integers is meant.

To proceed by reductio ad absurdum, suppose the polynomial is reducible. Formula (38.1) gives $a_0 = b_0c_0$. Since a_0 is divisible by p but not by p^2, either b_0 or c_0 is divisible by p but not both. It is a matter of notation to suppose $b_0 \equiv 0 \pmod{p}$. Since not all the coefficients of the polynomial f are divisible by p, there is at least one b not divisible by p. Let $b_0 \equiv \cdots \equiv b_{j-1} \equiv 0$, $b_j \not\equiv 0 \pmod{p}$. Formula (38.1) gives

$$(40.1) \quad a_j = b_jc_0 + b_{j-1}c_1 + \cdots + b_0c_j \quad (0 < j \leqq n < m),$$

and this equation reduces to $b_jc_0 \equiv 0$, or by Theorem 5.2 to $c_0 \equiv 0$, contrary to hypothesis. Hence the theorem is proved.

Taking $p = 2$, for example, shows that $x^2 - 2$ is irreducible and that consequently x is irrational if it is defined by

$$x^2 - 2 = 0.$$

Let us apply Eisenstein's result to

$$(40.2) \qquad f(x) = x^{p-1} + x^{p-2} + \cdots + x + 1,$$

where p is a prime.   As the equation stands, the theorem is not directly applicable. But $f(x)$ is irreducible if and only if $f(x + 1)$ is.   Moreover,

$$f(x) = \frac{x^p - 1}{x - 1}$$

so that

$$f(x + 1) = \frac{(x + 1)^p - 1}{x}.$$

To transform this, we note that the binomial coefficient

$$\frac{p(p - 1) \cdots (p - j + 1)}{j!} \qquad (j < p)$$

is divisible by p since it is an integer and no factor of $j!$ cancels into p.   Hence

(40.3) $(x + 1)^p \equiv x^p + 1 \qquad (\text{mod } p),$

so that

$$f(x + 1) \equiv x^{p-1} \qquad (\text{mod } p).$$

This means that all the coefficients of $f(x + 1)$ are divisible by p except the initial. The constant term of $f(x + 1)$ is $f(1) = p$ and hence is not divisible by p^2. Therefore $f(x + 1)$ is irreducible and as a consequence so is $f(x)$.

EXERCISES

40.1. Prove $x^2 + 1$ is irreducible in the ring of integers by using Eisenstein's theorem.

40.2. Treat $x^4 + 1$ in the same way.

Additional reading on polynomials will be found in B. L. van der Waerden's *Moderne Algebra*, Berlin, 1937, Chapter IV.

CHAPTER VI

GRAPHICAL METHODS

41. Coordinate Systems.—In a plane, a pair of directed perpendicular lines, taken in a definite order, and a unit of length determine a rectangular cartesian coordinate system. By means of it, with each point of the plane there is associated an ordered pair of real numbers (x, y). Conversely, to every

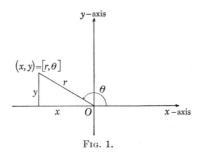

Fig. 1.

ordered pair of real numbers (x, y) there is a unique point in the plane.

The first of the two perpendicular lines is usually drawn horizontally with its positive direction pointing to the right. It is called the x-axis. The second of the perpendicular lines is drawn vertically, with positive direction upward, and is called the y-axis. The intersection of the two axes is the origin. The coordinates (x, y) of a point are then its distances from the two axes and are positive or negative according as they do or do not agree with the positive direction on the corresponding axis.

The points of the plane can also be specified by giving their *polar coordinates*, $[r, \theta]$, consisting of the *non-negative*[1] distance r of the point from the origin and the angle θ $(0 \leqq \theta < 2\pi)$ made with the positive x-axis by the line drawn from the origin to the point. The cartesian and polar coordinates are then related by the formulas

(41.1) $x = r \cos \theta, \qquad y = r \sin \theta.$

42. The Graph of an Equation.—One of the principal uses to which we shall apply the rectangular cartesian coordinate system is the graphical representation of an equation $y = f(x)$, where f is a polynomial with *real* coefficients.

To construct this graph, we assign x a series of values and compute the corresponding y's by synthetic division (Sec. 31). It is usually convenient to start by assigning x the integral values $0, \pm 1, \pm 2, \cdot \cdot \cdot$, to plot the resulting points, and then to interpolate fractional values of x where the general shape of the curve does not seem already to be clearly indicated.

Considerable information about the roots of the equation $f(x) = 0$ can be obtained by inspecting the graph of $y = f(x)$. These roots are the x's of the points where $y = 0$, that is, the intersections of the curve with the x-axis.

In the differential calculus it is proved that f' is the slope of the tangent to $y = f(x)$. In studying the shape of the curve, it is convenient to think of it as traced with x varying from $-\infty$ (numerically large negative numbers) to $+\infty$ (numerically large positive numbers), that is, with increasing x. With this understanding, the curve is rising or falling according as f' is positive or negative. If f' is zero, the tangent is parallel to the x-axis.

---

[1] Here it seems best to make the coordinates single-valued, although loci problems in analytic geometry require looser definition. If, as in complex variable, it is convenient to let the amplitude (Sec. 43) vary continuously when the point describes a circuit enclosing the origin, the amplitude employed here can be renamed "reduced amplitude."

It is convenient to plot the curve $y = f'(x)$, either on the same axes as $y = f(x)$, or with the same y-axis and different x-axis. Similarly for the higher derivatives. These curves

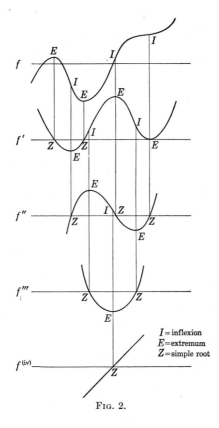

Fɪɢ. 2.

are called the *derived curves*. They are very useful in bringing out properties of f because they are interrelated. Thus f is rising, is falling or has a tangent parallel to the x-axis according as f' is above, below, or on the x-axis.

EXERCISES

Plot the graphs of the following polynomials and their derivatives, using a fixed y-axis and a different x-axis for each derived curve.

42.1. $x^3 - 6x^2 + 11x - 6$.   **42.2.** $x^4 - 5x^2 + 4$.

42.3. $x^4 + 2x^3 - x - 2$.   **42.4.** x^5.   **42.5.** x^6.

43. Graphical Representation of Complex Numbers.—A complex number is of the form $z = x + iy$, where x and y are real. Hence to every complex number z there corresponds a point whose cartesian coordinates are (x, y). The figure is called the *Argand diagram*.

The complex number can also be written in *polar form* by means of (41.1) as

$$(43.1) \qquad z = r(\cos \theta + i \sin \theta).$$

The non-negative number r is called the *modulus*[1] of z. It is given by the formula

$$(43.2) \qquad r = |z| = \sqrt{x^2 + y^2}.$$

When z is real, the modulus is $\pm z$ according as z is positive or negative. In the real case, it is often called the *absolute value* instead of the modulus (*cf.* footnote in Sec. 3). θ is called the *amplitude*.

The two complex numbers $z = x + iy$ and $\bar{z} = x - iy$ are called *conjugate complex*. They have the same modulus $|z| = |\bar{z}|$. The sum of their amplitudes is 2π, if they are imaginary. Their representative points are symmetrical with respect to the axis of reals. A complex z is real if and only if it is equal to its conjugate, $z = \bar{z}$.

Each of the two graphical representations has its particular advantages.

In the addition of complex numbers, the cartesian form is preferable. Thus the sum of $x_1 + iy_1$ and $x_2 + iy_2$ is

---

[1] This use of the term is totally distinct from that in Chapter I.

$$(x_1 + x_2) + i(y_1 + y_2),$$

and from the figure we see that the modulus of the sum is equal to the diagonal of a parallelogram whose two sides are the moduli of the summands.

From the fact that the sum of two sides of a triangle is never less than the third follows the important inequality

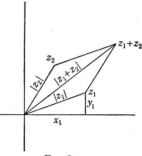

Fig. 3.

(43.3) $|z_1 + z_2| \leqq |z_1| + |z_2|,$

the equality sign holding only if the parallelogram flattens into a straight line.

On the other hand, where multiplication is concerned, the polar form is more convenient. Thus we have

$$z_1 z_2 = r_1 r_2 (\cos \theta_1 + i \sin \theta_1)(\cos \theta_2 + i \sin \theta_2).$$

Multiplying out the product of the parentheses gives

$$\cos \theta_1 \cos \theta_2 - \sin \theta_1 \sin \theta_2 + i(\sin \theta_1 \cos \theta_2 + \cos \theta_1 \sin \theta_2),$$

an expression which by means of the addition formulas of trigonometry can be written

$$\cos (\theta_1 + \theta_2) + i \sin (\theta_1 + \theta_2).$$

Accordingly, the cartesian coordinates of the point representing $z_1 z_2$ are

(43.4) $r_1 r_2 \cos (\theta_1 + \theta_2),$ $r_1 r_2 \sin (\theta_1 + \theta_2).$

If we substitute in (43.2), we find, since $(\text{sine})^2 + (\text{cosine})^2 = 1$,

(43.5) $|z_1 z_2| = |z_1| \cdot |z_2|.$

To get the amplitude of the product, we must find an angle θ satisfying $0 \leqq \theta < 2\pi$ and having the same terminal side as $\theta_1 + \theta_2$, that is, if $\theta_1 + \theta_2$ is greater than 2π, we subtract 2π

from it.   This is called *reducing* $\theta_1 + \theta_2$ modulo 2π in accordance with the terminology of congruences, although 2π is not a rational integer.

It is perhaps worth while to state (43.2), (43.3) in words as

Theorem 43.1.—*The modulus of a sum does not exceed the sum of the moduli of the terms.   The modulus of a product equals the product of the moduli of the factors.*

The following loci should be noted carefully, a being non-negative.

$$(43.6) \begin{cases} |z| = a & \text{Points on the circle of radius } a, \text{ center at} \\ & \text{the origin.} \\ |z| \leqq a & \text{Points on or interior to the above circle.} \\ |z| < a & \text{Points interior to the above circle.} \end{cases}$$

If we confine our attention to the real field, the representative points all lie along the x-axis.   If $a \neq 0$, the above circle cuts the real axis in two points.   Corresponding to the last two point sets (43.6) we have sets of points x satisfying

$$a \leqq x \leqq b, \qquad a < x < b.$$

The first of these is called an *interval;* the second is a *segment.* The difference between the two is that the end points a, b are included in the first, but not in the second.   Sets like

$$a \leqq x < b, \qquad a < x \leqq b$$

are also of importance.   We may obviously add sets of this last type to get every point on the line once and only once. Thus we see that the sets

$$-\infty < x \leqq -1, \qquad -1 < x \leqq 1, \qquad 1 < x \leqq \infty$$

exhaust those points.

Let the n or fewer roots which a polynomial has by Theorem 32.3 be plotted.   If a circle be drawn with center at one of them, say a, and passing through the nearest of the others b, there is no root of the polynomial within the circle.   Hence we have

THEOREM 43.2.—*The roots of a polynomial are isolated.*

The foregoing illustrates an important difference between polynomials and some more general types of function.   Consider, for example, the function defined for real $x \neq 0$ as

$$f(x) = x \sin \frac{1}{x},$$

and as zero for $x = 0$.   The root zero is not isolated.   For $\sin (1/x)$ vanishes when $x = 1/\pi, 1/(2\pi), \cdots, 1/(k\pi), \cdots$. There is an infinite number of these roots in every circle about the origin because $1/(k\pi)$ can be made as small as we please by taking the integer k large enough.

Let the distinct real roots of a polynomial f with real coefficients be arranged in increasing order of magnitude

$$x_1 < x_2 < x_3 < \cdots < x_l.$$

Then on each of the segments

(43.7) $\begin{matrix} -\infty < x < x_1, & x_1 < x < x_2, & \cdots , \\ x_{l-1} < x < x_l, & x_l < x < \infty \end{matrix}$

there is no root of f.   It will ultimately be proved (Sec. 73) that the sign of f is constant in each of these segments.

EXERCISES

43.1. By means of (43.2) transform (43.3) into an equivalent inequality between polynomials with real coefficients.   Hence give an algebraic proof of (43.3).

43.2. Prove $|z_1 + z_2| \geq |z_1| - |z_2|$.

43.3. Prove that if in a polynomial with non-negative coefficients the indeterminate is replaced by its modulus, the modulus of the polynomial is not decreased.

43.4. Prove (43.5) by substituting $z_1 = x_1 + iy_1$, $z_2 = x_2 + iy_2$ in it and reducing.

43.5. Prove that $z\bar{z} = |z|^2$.

43.6. Prove that the equation of the circle with center at α (a complex number) and radius a (a non-negative number) is

$$z\bar{z} - \alpha\bar{z} - \bar{\alpha}z + \alpha\bar{\alpha} = a^2.$$

43.7. A necessary and sufficient condition that z be pure imaginary is $\cdot + \bar{z} = 0$, $z \neq 0$.

44. De Moivre's Theorem.—Comparison of (41.1) and (43.4) shows the truth of

THEOREM 44.1.—*The amplitude of a product is the sum of the amplitudes reduced modulo* 2π.

This is in effect De Moivre's theorem.

Another way of regarding the matter follows. If all the points of the plane are subjected to a rotation through an angle φ about the origin, the point (x, y) goes into a point (x', y') given by the formulas

$$x' = x \cos \varphi - y \sin \varphi, \qquad y' = x \sin \varphi + y \cos \varphi,$$

which are proved in analytic geometry and which the reader should verify by constructing a figure. From them we readily get

$$z' = x' + iy' = (x + iy)(\cos \varphi + i \sin \varphi) = z(\cos \varphi + i \sin \varphi).$$

Hence

THEOREM 44.2.—*Multiplying a complex number by* $\cos \varphi + i \sin \varphi$ *rotates its representative point through the angle* φ *about the origin.*

As an immediate consequence of this, or of Theorem 44.1 we have

$$(44.1) \qquad (\cos \theta + i \sin \theta)^n = \cos n\theta + i \sin n\theta,$$

for all positive integers n.   The formula is readily extended to all rational numbers and such is the usual form of De Moivre's theorem.

It can be shown[1] by the use of infinite series that

$$(44.2) \qquad e^{i\theta} = \cos\theta + i\sin\theta,$$

a formula which makes De Moivre's theorem immediately obvious: to raise $e^{i\theta}$ to a power, we need only multiply its exponent, $i\theta$, by the exponent of the power.

EXERCISES

Evaluate the following expressions:

44.1. $e^{\pi i}$.   **44.2.** $e^{2\pi i}$.   **44.3.** $\left| e^{i\theta} \right|$.

44.4. $e^{\frac{1}{2}\pi i}$.

44.5. From the identity $(\cos\theta + i\sin\theta)^3 = \cos 3\theta + i\sin 3\theta$ find expressions for $\sin 3\theta$, $\cos 3\theta$.

45. Polynomials for Small Values of the Indeterminate.— Consider the polynomial

$$(45.1) \quad f(x) = a_0 x^n + a_1 x^{n-1} + \cdots + a_{n-1}x + a_n,$$

for complex values of the a's and x.   By (43.3) we have

$$|f(x) - a_n| \leqq |a_0 x^n| + |a_1 x^{n-1}| + \cdots + |a_{n-1}x|,$$

or when use is made of (43.5),

$$(45.2) \quad |f(x) - a_n| \leqq |a_0| \cdot |x|^n + \\ |a_1| \cdot |x|^{n-1} + \cdots + |a_{n-1}| \cdot |x|.$$

If we choose a positive A sufficiently large to satisfy

$$|a_0| \leqq A, \qquad |a_1| \leqq A, \qquad \cdots, \qquad |a_{n-1}| \leqq A,$$

then the inequality (45.2) persists if the modulus of each a_j is replaced by A.   Hence

$$(45.3) \quad |f(x) - a_n| \leqq A(|x|^n + |x|^{n-1} + \cdots + |x|).$$

---

[1] H. B. Fine, *Calculus*, New York, 1933, p. 405.

If $|x| < 1$, then $|x|^k \leqq |x|$ for all positive k, so that the expression in parentheses does not exceed $n|x|$. Accordingly, when $|x|$ satisfies the two inequalities

$$|x| < \frac{\epsilon}{nA}, \qquad |x| < 1,$$

(45.3) becomes

$$|f(x) - a_n| < \epsilon.$$

Another way of writing this is

(45.4) $|f(x) - f(0)| < \epsilon.$

If we regard x as constant, the $f(x + h)$ given by (33.1) becomes a polynomial in h with constant term $f(x)$. Hence for it (45.4) is

(45.5) $|f(x + h) - f(x)| < \epsilon,$

or in slightly different notation

(45.6) $|f(x) - f(a)| < \epsilon,$

provided $|x - a|$ is sufficiently small. Because of the property expressed by (45.6), a polynomial is called *continuous*. Roughly speaking, this means that a small change in x induces only a small change in $f(x)$.

Consider the plane in which x is represented by a point and plot $f(x)$ as a point in a second plane. If a circle C with arbitrary radius be drawn about $f(x)$, then a circle c can be drawn about x such that $f(x + h)$ lies within C whenever the point $x + h$ lies within c. In particular, if $f(x) \neq 0$, we can draw the circle C with center at $f(x)$ and passing through zero. For values of x within the corresponding c, $f(x)$ will be within C and will therefore be different from zero. If this is applied to the case of reals, each point at which f does not have a root can be placed in a segment on which f does not have a root.

The extremities of the maximum segment with this property must be roots of f. Compare (43.7).

45.1. Find a segment $-\delta < x < \delta$ in which

$$3.9 < |2x^2 - 3x + 4| < 4.1.$$

45.2. Find a segment $-\delta < x - 1 < \delta$ in which

$$6.99 < |2x^3 + x + 4| < 7.01.$$

45.3. Find a circle $|z - 1| < \delta$ in which

$$1.3 < |z^4 + (1 + i)z - 1| < 1.5.$$

46. Consequences of the Taylor Development.—Formula (33.1) is the Taylor development for the polynomial f. Replacing $x + h$ by x and x by a, we rewrite it in the form

$$(46.1) \quad f(x) = f(a) + (x - a)f'(a) + \frac{(x - a)^2}{2!}f''(a)$$
$$+ \cdots + \frac{(x - a)^n}{n!}f^{(n)}(a).$$

If a is a root of multiplicity k, by Sec. 34

$$f(a) = f'(a) = \cdots = f^{(k-1)}(a) = 0, \qquad f^{(k)}(a) \neq 0.$$

Then

$$\frac{k!f(x)}{(x - a)^k} = f^{(k)}(a) + \varphi(x - a),$$

where φ is a polynomial with constant term zero. By taking $|x - a|$ small enough, φ can be made as near zero as we like. so that the right member has the sign of $f^{(k)}(a)$. From this follows

THEOREM 46.1.—*If a is a k-fold real root of an equation $f = 0$ with real coefficients,*

(46.2) $\qquad f(x) \qquad$ *and* $\qquad (x - a)^k f^{(k)}(a)$

agree in sign on $b < x < a$ and on $a < x < c$, where b, c are numbers sufficiently near to a.

Thus in the real case $f(x)$ and $(x - a)^k f^{(k)}(a)$ have the same sign for values of x near a. If k is odd, the factor $(x - a)^k$

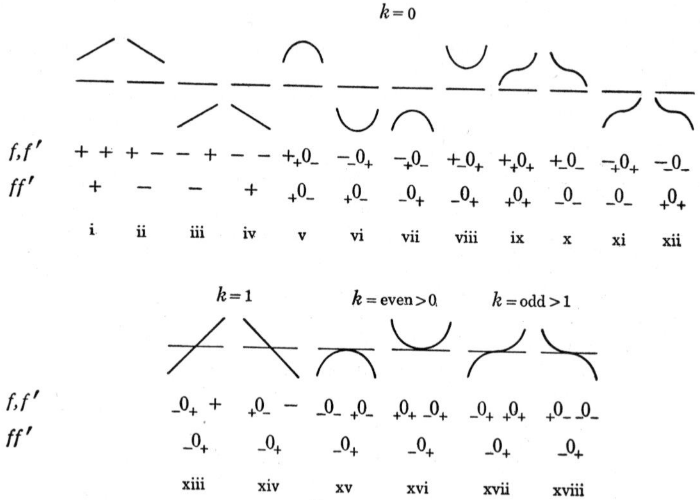

Fig. 4.

changes sign as x increases through a. If k is even, $(x - a)^k$ is positive. Consequently, *the curve crosses the x-axis at $x = a$ if and only if k is odd.*

If $k = 0$, then $f(a)$ is not zero and the curve does not meet the axis at $x = a$. See i to xii in Fig. 4, where the notation

$$\varphi(a) = {}_+0_-$$

means that φ is zero at a and changes sign from $+$ to $-$ there.

If $k = 1$, the curve intersects the x-axis at $x = a$ at a non-zero angle, xiii, xiv in the figure.

If $k > 1$, at least two roots are equal to a, $f'(a) = 0$ and the curve is tangent to the axis, xv to xviii in the figure.

If $k = 2$, the curve is tangent to the x-axis for $x = a$ and lies entirely below it or above it in the vicinity. Similarly for any even $k > 0$. Besides representing a root, such a point is an *extremum* (maximum or minimum), xv, xvi in the figure.

If $k = 3$, the curve is tangent to the axis and crosses it. Similarly for any odd $k > 1$. Such a point is an *inflexion*, xvii, xviii in the figure.

The configurations at v, vi concave toward the axis will be called *humps*. The test for a hump is evidently

$$f \neq 0, \qquad ff' = {}_+0_-.$$

Similarly, vii, viii will be called *depressions*. The condition for one is

$$f \neq 0, \qquad ff' = {}_-0_+.$$

It will be noted that if $k > 0$, $ff' = {}_-0_+$, that is,

THEOREM 46.2.[1]—*If the coefficients of f are real, the polynomial ff' changes sign from minus to plus as x increases through a root of f.*

The foregoing useful result is intuitively obvious. If f is positive before a root, for example, the curve must go down, that is, f' must be negative, in order that f reach the axis. Hence ff' is negative before. If f is negative before, the curve must go up, that is, f' must be positive, and we have the same conclusion. After the root, the curve must leave the axis, and to do this rises or falls according as it is above or below.

EXERCISE

46.1. Prove Theorem 46.2 by considering the polynomial f^2, which is non-negative.

[1] A. Hurwitz, Mathematische Annalen, vol. 71 (1912), p. 585.

47. Polynomials for Large Values of the Indeterminate.—
Rewrite the polynomial f as

$$f(x) = a_0 x^n \left(1 + \frac{a_1}{a_0}\frac{1}{x} + \cdots + \frac{a_{n-1}}{a_0}\frac{1}{x^{n-1}} + \frac{a_n}{a_0}\frac{1}{x^n} \right)$$

so that the quotient

$$\frac{f(x)}{a_0 x^n}$$

is a polynomial in $1/x$. From Sec. 45 the modulus of the
difference between this polynomial and its constant term 1
can be made as small as we please by taking $1/|x|$ small
enough, that is. by taking $|x|$ large enough. Hence

(47.1) $$\left| \frac{f(x)}{a_0 x^n} - 1 \right| < \epsilon$$

provided $|x| > N$, where N is a sufficiently large number.

In particular, when the coefficients of f are real and x is
given only real values, *the polynomial $f(x)$ has the same sign as
its leader when x has sufficiently large absolute value.*

Thus we have the results:

(i) n even, a_0 positive: the curve is above the x-axis for x
numerically large.

(ii) n even, a_0 negative: the curve is below the axis for x
numerically large.

(iii) n odd, a_0 positive: the curve is below the axis for large
negative x and above it for large positive x.

(iv) n odd, a_0 negative: the curve is above the axis for
large negative x and below it for large positive x.

CHAPTER VII

ROOTS OF UNITY

The equations studied in this chapter, although of very special form, nevertheless merit separate systematic treatment because of their importance and because of the perfection which their theory can readily be given. The results are mostly formal and some of them (Sec. 50, 51) apply even when x is a permutation, for example.

48. Unity Has n nth Roots.—The equation to be studied is

$$(48.1) \qquad x^n = 1,$$

where n is a positive integer. The equation is obviously satisfied by $x = +1$ for all values of n, and by $x = -1$, if n is even. From (43.5), $|x|^n = 1$ and since $|x| \geqq 0$, we have $|x| = 1$. Hence the roots of unity all lie on a circle of unit radius with center at the origin. The only possible real roots of unity correspond to the points where this circle meets the axis of reals, namely, ± 1.

From (44.2) we have

$$(48.2) \qquad e^{\frac{2\pi i}{n}} = \cos \frac{2\pi}{n} + i \sin \frac{2\pi}{n}.$$

By De Moivre's theorem, the nth power of this is unity. Hence (48.2) is an nth root of unity. Call it α. Then α^k is an nth root of unity because $(\alpha^k)^n = (\alpha^n)^k = 1$. By De Moivre's theorem,

$$(48.3) \qquad 1, \qquad \alpha, \qquad \alpha^2, \qquad \cdots, \qquad \alpha^{n-1}$$

have amplitudes $0, 2\pi/n, \cdots, 2\pi(n-1)/n$ and hence are distinct. Since the equation has at most n roots by Theorem 32.3, the roots are given by (48.3), and we have

Theorem 48.1.—*Unity has n distinct nth roots. The only real nth roots are ± 1 for n even and $+1$ for n odd.*

EXERCISES

48.1. Find the fourth roots of unity by using (48.2).
48.2. Find the sixth roots of unity by using (48.2).

49. The Cube Roots of Unity.—From the identity

$$x^3 - 1 = (x - 1)(x^2 + x + 1)$$

it follows that the two imaginary cube roots of unity satisfy

$$(49.1) \qquad x^2 + x + 1 = 0.$$

Let ω be one of them. As in Sec. 48, the second root is ω^2. Since $(\omega^2)^2 = \omega^4 = \omega \cdot \omega^3 = \omega$, we have the important result contained in

Theorem 49.1.—*Unity has two imaginary cube roots which satisfy the quadratic equation*

$$(49.2) \qquad \omega^2 + \omega + 1 = 0.$$

Each root is simultaneously the conjugate, the reciprocal and the square of the other.

The three cube roots of unity 1, ω, ω^2 can be employed in seeking the cube roots which it will appear later any complex number A has. Thus the equation $x^3 - A = 0$ has three roots, which are distinct, except when $A = 0$, because the derivative $3x^2$ vanishes only for $x = 0$. If α is one of the roots, then

$$(49.3) \qquad \alpha, \qquad \alpha\omega, \qquad \alpha\omega^2$$

are evidently the set of three because they are distinct and have cube equal to A.

If A is real, the root α can be taken as the real cube root and so the three roots are easily expressed in the form $a + bi$ by (49.3). If α is imaginary, however, as we shall see later (Sec. 70) the cube roots cannot always be obtained by algebraic methods in entirely satisfactory form.

EXERCISES

49.1. Find the two imaginary cube roots of unity by performing (Sec. 31) the division $(x^3 - 1)/(x - 1)$ and solving the resulting quadratic equation.

49.2. Find the imaginary fourth roots in similar fashion.

50. Period of Roots.—Theorem 10.1 leads us to define the period of any symbol C as the positive integer p (if it exists) satisfying $C^p = 1$ and $C^k \neq 1$ for $0 < k < p$. The root α given by (48.2), for example, has period n. Any nth root of unity has a period which obviously cannot exceed n. Actually, we can go farther and prove

THEOREM 50.1.—*The period of a root of unity is a divisor of the degree of the equation.*

To show this, let the highest common factor of the period p and the degree n be k, so that $p = kl$, $n = km$, where l, m are relatively prime. By Theorem 3.2 we can determine integers a, b so that $al + bm = 1$, whence, by multiplication by k, $ap + bn = k$. Consequently, if α is the root in question

$$\alpha^k = \alpha^{ap+bn} = (\alpha^p)^a(\alpha^n)^b = 1.$$

Since by definition p is the minimum positive integer for which $\alpha^p = 1$, we must have $k \geqq p$. But $k \leqq p$. Hence $k = p$, and p divides n because k does.

Theorem 50.1 is, in fact, the analogue of Theorem 10.3. For if α has period p and $\alpha^n = 1$, then by Theorem 50.1 $n \equiv 0 \pmod{p}$.

51. Multiplication of Roots.—Let α be a kth root and β an lth root. Since

$$(\alpha\beta)^{kl} = (\alpha^k)^l(\beta^l)^k = 1,$$

the product is a klth root. Thus the product of a square root and a cube root is necessarily a sixth root; but since the period may vary, it is convenient to establish the more precise result contained in

Theorem 51.1.—*If α, β are roots of relatively prime periods, k, l, then $\alpha\beta$ is a root of period kl. Conversely, every root of period kl, where k and l are relatively prime, is the product of a root of period k by a root of period l.*

To prove the first part of the theorem we remark that the period of $\alpha\beta$ is a divisor of kl. It can therefore (Theorem 3.4) be written as $k_1 l_1$, where $k = k_1 k_2$, $l = l_1 l_2$. If we raise

$$\alpha^{k_1 l_1}\beta^{k_1 l_1} = 1$$

to the l_2th and k_2th powers, we get

$$\alpha^{k_1 l} = 1, \qquad \beta^{k l_1} = 1.$$

Hence by Theorem 50.1 $k_1 l \equiv 0 \pmod{k}$, $kl_1 \equiv 0 \pmod{l}$. Since k, l are relatively prime, Theorem 5.2 gives $k_1 \equiv 0 \pmod{k}$, $l_1 \equiv 0 \pmod{l}$, that is, $k = k_1$, $l = l_1$.

Conversely, if k, l are relatively prime, let (Theorem 3.2) p, q be integers such that $kp + lq = 1$. Then

(51.1) $$\gamma = \gamma^{kp}\gamma^{lq}.$$

If γ is a root of period kl, then γ^{kp} is an lth root. If its period were less than l, from (51.1) the period of γ would be less than kl. Similarly, the period of γ^{lq} is k.

52. Primitive Roots.—An nth root of period n is called a *primitive nth root*. Such a root satisfies no equation like (48.1) of degree lower than n. Thus -1 is a primitive square root because it does not satisfy $x = 1$; and the two imaginary cube roots of Exercise 49.1 are primitive because they satisfy neither $x = 1$ nor $x^2 = 1$. On the other hand, -1 although a fourth root is not a primitive fourth root because it also satisfies $x^2 = 1$. The α of (48.2) is a primitive nth root.

EXERCISE

52.1. If ω is an imaginary cube root of unity, $-\omega$ is a primitive sixth root of unity. Find all the primitive sixth roots of unity.

53. All the nth Roots Expressed in Terms of a Primitive Root.—We next prove the useful

THEOREM 53.1.—*The nth roots of unity can be written*

$$(53.1) \qquad 1, \quad \alpha, \quad \alpha^2, \quad \cdots, \quad \alpha^{n-1},$$

where α is any primitive nth root.

It is clear that (53.1) are nth roots because

$$(\alpha^i)^n = (\alpha^n)^i = 1.$$

They are all distinct because

$$\alpha^j = \alpha^k, \qquad j > k,$$

would imply

$$\alpha^{j-k} = 1,$$

so that the period of α would not exceed the positive $j - k < n$. Since there are n of them, they must be the nth roots written in some order and the theorem is proved.

For the above reason, a primitive root is said to *generate* the set of nth roots. This property is characteristic: a non-primitive root satisfies an equation $x^k = 1$ with $k < n$ so that it has less than n distinct powers.

54. Number of Primitive Roots.—In (53.1) let the period of α^i be p. Then $jp \equiv 0 \pmod{n}$ by Theorem 50.1 applied to the

root α of the equation $\alpha^{jp} = 1$. Let $j = qj_1$, $n = qn_1$, where j_1, n_1 are relatively prime. Theorem 5.2 gives $p \equiv 0 \pmod{n_1}$. On the other hand,

$$(\alpha^j)^{n_1} = (\alpha^n)^{j_1} = 1,$$

so that $n_1 \equiv 0 \pmod{p}$. Hence $p = n_1$.

THEOREM 54.1.—*If α is a primitive nth root of unity, the period of α^j is obtained by removing from n the highest common factor of n and j.*

THEOREM 54.2.—*The jth power of a primitive root is also a primitive root if and only if n and j are relatively prime.*

The primitive roots in (53.1) accordingly correspond to the exponents in (53.1) which are prime to n, and we have (Sec. 6)

THEOREM 54.3.—*The number of primitive nth roots of unity is $\phi(n)$.*

An illustration follows. If ω and i are primitive cube and fourth roots, respectively, $\alpha = \omega i$ is a primitive twelfth root by Theorem 51.1. Its powers and their periods are shown below.

α	α^2	α^3	α^4	α^5	α^6	α^7	α^8	α^9	α^{10}	α^{11}	α^{12}
ωi	$-\omega^2$	$-i$	ω	$\omega^2 i$	-1	$-\omega i$	ω^2	i	$-\omega$	$-\omega^2 i$	1
12	6	4	3	12	2	12	3	4	6	12	1

The number of primitive twelfth roots is thus seen directly to be $4 = 12(1 - \frac{1}{2})(1 - \frac{1}{3})$.

EXERCISE

54.1. By using Theorems 51.1 and 54.3 give another proof of Theorem 6.1.

55. Graphical Representation.—We saw above (Sec. 48) that in the Argand diagram the roots of unity all lie on the unit circle, that is, the circle of unit radius with center at the origin.

The diagram is symmetric with respect to the x-axis, that is, the roots occur in conjugate pairs. This illustrates Theorem 63.1, to be proved later.

If n is even, there is also symmetry with respect to the y-axis and the origin. The roots can be grouped in pairs α, $-\alpha$.

EXERCISE

55.1. Plot the cube, fourth, and sixth roots of unity on diagrams. Find approximate values for them from the figure.

56. The Equation Satisfied by All the Primitive nth Roots.— The sixth roots of unity are the roots of

$$x^6 - 1 = 0.$$

Included among them are the first root, the square roots, and the cube roots, corresponding to the factors 1, 2, 3 of 6. These must be eliminated, if we wish the equation satisfied by the primitive roots alone. The expression

$$\frac{x^6 - 1}{x^3 - 1}$$

has the cube roots eliminated. The square roots satisfy $x^2 - 1 = 0$. Hence we divide by that factor. But this means that the factor $(x - 1)$ corresponding to 1, which is both a square root and a cube root, has been eliminated twice. So we restore it in the numerator and obtain finally

$$\frac{(x^6 - 1)(x - 1)}{(x^3 - 1)(x^2 - 1)} = x^2 - x + 1.$$

The degree of this is $\phi(6) = 2$, as it should be.

The same method obviously applies to every degree. In applying it, we need only be careful to eliminate each imprimitive root once and only once.

The coefficients in the resulting equation can be proved integral. In addition, it is known that for $n < 105$ every coefficient in the resulting equation has one of the three values $-1, 0, 1$. I. Schur, however, has proved[1] that an equation with arbitrarily large coefficients can be obtained by taking n large enough.

A simple proof that the equations of this section are irreducible is given by Weber.[2]

EXERCISES

Find the equations satisfied by all the primitive nth roots of unity in each of the following cases:

56.1. $n = 8$.   **56.2.** $n = 9$.   **56.3.** $n = 10$.
56.4. $n = 12$.   **56.5.** $n = 15$.

57. Irreducibility of the Cyclotomic Equation.—Because of Theorem 51.1, to find the nth roots of unity, we need only consider the equations corresponding to the relatively prime factors $p_1^{e_1}, p_2^{e_2}, \cdots, p_m^{e_m}$ (Sec. 4) of the degree n.

Any p^eth root, where p is a prime, is primitive unless it is a p^{e-1}th root. Consequently the primitive roots satisfy

$$(57.1) \quad f(x) = \frac{x^{p^e} - 1}{x^{p^{e-1}} - 1} = x^{p^{e-1}(p-1)} + x^{p^{e-1}(p-2)}$$
$$+ \cdots + x^{p^{e-1}} + 1 = 0.$$

Because of the geometric representation of the roots of unity, (57.1) is called the *cyclotomic equation*. For $e = 1$, it has already been proved irreducible (Sec. 40). Next we shall prove the more general

[1] *Cf.* E. Lehmer, Bulletin of the American Math. Soc., vol. 42 (1936), pp. 389–392.

[2] *Lehrbuch der Algebra*, vol. I, pp. 596–600.

THEOREM 57.1.—*The cyclotomic equation* (57.1) *is irreducible in the rational field.*

Suppose f is reducible and $f = gh$, where g, h belong to $\mathcal{I}[x]$ (*cf.* p. 66). Evaluation for $x = 1$ gives $p = g(1)h(1)$. Hence we may take $g(1) = +1$. Let $j_1, j_2, \cdots, j_l$ be the $l = \phi(p^e)$ positive integers prime to p^e and less than it. Let

$$k(x) = g(x^{j_1})g(x^{j_2}) \cdots g(x^{j_l}).$$

If α is any root of (57.1), then $\alpha^{j_1}, \alpha^{j_2}, \cdots, \alpha^{j_l}$ represent all the primitive roots of $x^{p^e} - 1 = 0$, that is, all the roots of (57.1). Now $g(x) = 0$ is satisfied by at least one of these roots. Hence in

$$k(\alpha) = g(\alpha^{j_1})g(\alpha^{j_2}) \cdots g(\alpha^{j_l})$$

at least one factor on the right is zero, that is, every root of $f(x) = 0$ is a root of $k(x) = 0$. Therefore, by Theorem 37.1,

$$(57.2) \qquad k(x) = f(x)q(x).$$

Theorem 39.1 shows that the coefficients of q are integers.

Evaluating (57.2) for $x = 1$ gives $1 = pq(1)$. Since $q(1)$ is an integer, this is impossible. The assumption that f is reducible therefore leads to a contradiction and is false.

58. Binomial Equations.—The general form of a binomial equation, that is, an equation with two terms, is

$$ax^m + bx^n = 0, \qquad ab \neq 0,$$

where we may assume $m > n$. Division by ax^n gives

$$x^{m-n} + a^{-1}b = 0,$$

which is of the form

$$(58.1) \qquad x^n = a.$$

If one root β of this equation is known, the n roots are

(58.2) $\beta,$ $\alpha\beta,$ $\alpha^2\beta,$ $\cdots,$ $\alpha^{n-1}\beta,$

where α is a primitive nth root of unity.

In particular, if a is positive, β can be taken as the positive nth root; if a is real and n odd, it can be taken as the real nth root (whose sign is the same as that of a).

59. An Irreducible Binomial Equation.—We shall next prove

Theorem 59.1.—*The polynomial $x^p - a$, where p is prime and a belongs to a field $\mathfrak{F}$ but is not the pth power of a member of $\mathfrak{F}$, is irreducible in $\mathfrak{F}$.*

Let $x^p - a$ have a factor f of degree q $(0 < q < p)$ with coefficients in $\mathfrak{F}$ and initial 1. Then q of the roots (58.2) satisfy $f = 0$. Their product, which is of the form $\alpha^r\beta^q$, belongs to $\mathfrak{F}$. Since p, q are relatively prime, integers λ, μ can be determined (Theorem 3.2) so that $-\lambda p + \mu q = 1$. Then

$$(\alpha^r\beta^q)^\mu = \alpha^{r\mu}\beta^{q\mu} = \alpha^{r\mu}\beta^{1+\lambda p} = \alpha^{r\mu}\beta a^\lambda.$$

Since this number and a^λ are in $\mathfrak{F}$, so also is $\alpha^{r\mu}\beta$, which is a root of $x^p - a$. Thus a is the pth power of a quantity, $\alpha^{r\mu}\beta$, which is in the field, contrary to hypothesis, and the theorem is proved.

For further reading, H. Weber's *Lehrbuch der Algebra*, vol. 1, Chapter XII; R. Fricke's *Lehrbuch der Algebra*, vol. 1, Braunschweig, 1924, Chapter V, can be consulted.

CHAPTER VIII

SINGLE EQUATION IN SINGLE UNKNOWN

60. The Fundamental Theorem of Algebra.—We shall assume as a postulate the following theorem, whose proof is most readily accomplished by non-algebraic methods and will be found, for example, in treatises on the theory of functions of a complex variable.[1]

THEOREM 60.1.—*Every polynomial whose degree is at least one and whose coefficients are complex has a complex root.*

Let x_1 be a root of $f(x)$. By the factor theorem

$$f(x) = (x - x_1)f_1(x),$$

where f_1 is a polynomial of degree $n - 1$. Its coefficients are formed from the original complex coefficients by the operations $+$, $-$, $\times$, and they are complex because the complex numbers form a ring.

If $n - 1 > 0$, $f_1(x)$ has a root x_2, and can be written

$$f_1(x) = (x - x_2)f_2(x).$$

This process can be continued as long as the degree is positive. The last quotient will be of degree zero, so that it reduces to its initial. But since the initial of each divisor is unity, the initial of every quotient is the same as that of f, namely, a_0. Hence

$$f_{n-1}(x) = (x - x_n)a_0.$$

---

[1] A proof which does not presuppose a knowledge of the theory of functions is given in H. B. Fine's *College Algebra*, pp. 588–589.

93

Direct substitution gives

$$(60.1) \qquad f(x) = a_0(x - x_1)(x - x_2) \cdots (x - x_n).$$

We have, therefore,

> **Theorem 60.2.**—*The equation $f(x) = 0$, where f is a polynomial with complex coefficients and with degree n, has exactly n roots. All of them are complex numbers.*

Some of the roots may, of course, be equal.

61. Relations between the Roots and the Coefficients.—We suppose the initial $a_0 = 1$, a condition which can always be realized by dividing by a_0, if necessary. Then (60.1) becomes

$$(61.1) \qquad f(x) = (x - x_1)(x - x_2) \cdots (x - x_n).$$

Let us perform the multiplication indicated on the right side of this equation. Each term in the product will contain one and only one letter from each of the n pairs of parentheses. The product, moreover, is the sum of all terms which can be formed by taking one letter from each pair of parentheses.

If x is chosen from all n pairs, the unique term x^n results.

If x is chosen from exactly $n - 1$ pairs, the x_j must be chosen from the remaining pair and a term of the type $-x_1 x^{n-1}$ results. Since the x_j can be chosen from each of the n pairs, the totality of such terms is

$$-x_1 x^{n-1} - x_2 x^{n-1} - \cdots - x_n x^{n-1},$$

or, as we shall write it,

$$-(\Sigma x_1) x^{n-1},$$

the Σ standing for the sum of all terms of which x_1 is the type.

If x is chosen from exactly $n - 2$ pairs, we must take the x_j from each of the remaining two pairs. A term of the type $(-x_1)(-x_2) x^{n-2}$ results. The totality of such terms is

$$(\Sigma x_1 x_2)x^{n-2}.$$

Note that when two x_j's are taken, the minus signs cancel and give plus.

Proceeding in this way we get

$$(61.2) \qquad \begin{aligned} f(x) = x^n &- (\Sigma x_1)x^{n-1} + (\Sigma x_1 x_2)x^{n-2} \\ &- (\Sigma x_1 x_2 x_3)x^{n-3} + \cdots \\ &+ (-1)^{n-1}(\Sigma x_1 x_2 \cdots x_{n-1})x \\ &+ (-1)^n x_1 x_2 \cdots x_n. \end{aligned}$$

No sigma sign is necessary in the last term, because there is only one such product.

When the initial is unity, the coefficient of x^{n-k} is $\pm$ the sum of all the products of the roots taken k at a time, the sign being plus or minus according as k is even or odd.

Thus for the cubic

$$x^3 + \beta x^2 + \gamma x + \delta$$

we have

$$-\beta = x_1 + x_2 + x_3, \qquad \gamma = x_2 x_3 + x_3 x_1 + x_1 x_2,$$
$$-\delta = x_1 x_2 x_3.$$

The cubic

$$ax^3 + bx^2 + cx + d$$

must be written

$$x^3 + \frac{b}{a}x^2 + \frac{c}{a}x + \frac{d}{a}$$

before being treated.   We thus have

$$-\frac{b}{a} = x_1 + x_2 + x_3, \qquad \frac{c}{a} = x_2 x_3 + x_3 x_1 + x_1 x_2,$$
$$-\frac{d}{a} = x_1 x_2 x_3.$$

The coefficients in (61.2) are called the *elementary symmetric polynomials in the roots.*

The result developed in this section can be used to find the equation having a given set of roots. For example, let the proposed roots be 1, −2, 3, 4. Their sum is 6. To get the sum of the products two at a time, we multiply the root 1 in turn by each root that follows it and obtain −2 + 3 + 4 = 5. Then we multiply −2 by each that follows it, getting −6 − 8 = −14. Then 3 by each that follows it, obtaining 12. Hence the sum of the products two at a time is 5 − 14 + 12 = 3. To get a product of three, we have to omit one root from the four. Omitting each in succession gives −24 + 12 − 8 − 6 = −26. Finally, the product of all the roots is −24, so that the equation is

$$x^4 - 6x^3 + 3x^2 + 26x - 24 = 0.$$

Synthetic division should be employed to check the result.

EXERCISES

Find equations with integral coefficients having the roots given below.

61.1. 1, 2.　　　　　　**61.2.** 1, 2, 3.　　　　　**61.3.** 1, 2, 3, 4.
61.4. 1, −2, 3, −4.　　　　　　**61.5.** $\frac{1}{2}$, 1, −1.
61.6. 1, 1 + *i*, 1 − *i*.　　　　　**61.7.** $\frac{3}{2}$, −$\frac{1}{2}$, 1, −$\frac{1}{3}$.
61.8. 1, 1, 2, 2.

Find the elementary symmetric polynomials for each of the following:

61.9. $2x^2 - 3x + 4$.
61.10. $x^3 - x + 5$.
61.11. $3x^4 - 2x^2 + 4x - 1$.
61.12. $x^4 - 1$.

62. Rational Roots.—The results in this section will apply only to equations whose *coefficients are rational.* Let

$$f(x) = a_0 x^n + a_1 x^{n-1} + \cdots + a_{n-1} x + a_n = 0$$

be an equation with *integral coefficients*, and let it have a rational root *r/s*, where *r* and *s* are relatively prime (Sec. 2) integers. Substitution gives

$$\frac{a_0 r^n}{s^n} + \frac{a_1 r^{n-1}}{s^{n-1}} + \cdots + \frac{a_{n-1} r}{s} + a_n = 0.$$

Multiply this result by s^{n-1} and by s^n/r and transpose to obtain

(62.1) $$-\frac{a_0 r^n}{s} = a_1 r^{n-1} + \cdots + a_n s^{n-1},$$

(62.2) $$-\frac{a_n s^n}{r} = a_0 r^{n-1} + \cdots + a_{n-1} s^{n-1}.$$

The right members of these equations are formed from integers by the ring operations $+$, $-$, $\times$. Hence they are integers. Since r^n and s are relatively prime, Theorem 3.4 applied to (62.1) shows that s is a factor of a_0. Similarly, (62.2) shows that r is a factor of a_n. We have therefore

THEOREM 62.1.—*If a rational root of an equation with integral coefficients is put in its lowest terms, its numerator is a divisor of the constant term and its denominator is a divisor of the initial. If the initial is unity, any rational root is necessarily integral.*

Hence it is easy to find a set of rational numbers among which are included all rational roots of a given equation.

THEOREM 62.2.—*It can be determined by a finite number of trials whether an equation with rational coefficients has a rational root.*

Thus if the equation is

$$6x^3 + x + 4 = 0,$$

the only possible rational roots are

$$\pm 1, \quad \pm 2, \quad \pm 4, \quad \pm \tfrac{1}{2}, \quad \pm \tfrac{1}{3}, \quad \pm \tfrac{2}{3}, \quad \pm \tfrac{4}{3}, \quad \pm \tfrac{1}{6}.$$

Which of these actually satisfy the equation can be determined by synthetic substitution. To test $\frac{1}{2}$, for example, we divide by $2x - 1$, that is, we use the synthetic divisor $2 + 1$. It is not necessary to multiply the dividend by b_0^{m-n+1} as in Sec. 30 to avoid fractions. To see this, suppose that the given polynomial is af, where a is an integer and f is a unit polynomial, and that the rational number in its lowest terms is r/s. By Theorem 39.1 the coefficients of the quotient $f/(sx - r)$, and hence those of $af/(sx - r)$, are integers, if the division is exact. This not only establishes the desired point, but in addition proves that *the substitution can be immediately halted if a fractional coefficient is encountered because it is then known that the rational number is not a root.*

When the root r/s has been obtained, it is in general easiest to continue the test on the quotient $f/(sx - r)$, which is called the *depressed polynomial*.

EXERCISES

Find by trial the rational roots of the following:

62.1. $2x^3 + 3x^2 + 3x + 1$.

62.2. $6x^4 - 7x^3 + 6x^2 - 1$.

62.3. $12x^4 + 19x^3 - 12x^2 - 13x + 6$.

62.4. $3x^3 - 3x + 1$.

62.5. $48x^4 - 76x^3 - 12x^2 + 31x - 6$.

63. Imaginary Roots.—The results in this section apply only to equations with *real coefficients*. If $a + bi$ is an imaginary root of such an equation, we wish to prove that the conjugate imaginary $a - bi$ is also a root.

We first form by the method of Sec. 61 a quadratic polynomial vanishing for $a \pm bi$. It is easily found to be

$$g(x) = x^2 - 2ax + a^2 + b^2$$

and obviously has real coefficients. By the division process we can write

$$(63.1) \qquad f(x) = g(x)Q(x) + cx + d,$$

the remainder being linear in form because the divisor is quadratic.   The numbers c, d are real because they are formed by ring operations from real numbers.

Substitution of $x = a + bi$ in (63.1) gives

$$(63.2) \qquad 0 = ca + cbi + d.$$

$ca + d$ is real because it is formed by ring operations from reals.   Its equal $-cbi$ is either pure imaginary or zero.   Hence $cbi = 0$.   Since $a + bi$ is imaginary, $b \neq 0$, and therefore $c = 0$.   From (63.2) it follows that $d = 0$.

Hence from (63.1) we see that $f(x)$ is divisible by $g(x)$ and has therefore both roots of $g(x)$.

THEOREM 63.1.—*In an equation with real coefficients, imaginary roots occur in conjugate pairs.*

EXERCISE

63.1. Find the equation with real coefficients and lowest possible degree satisfied by $1 + i$ and i.

64. Quadratic Surd Roots.—Consider now equations with *rational coefficients*, and let[1] $a + \sqrt{b}$, where a is rational and b is rational but not the square of a rational number (and consequently not zero), be a root of $f(x) = 0$.   The conjugate *quadratic surds* $a \pm \sqrt{b}$ are roots of

$$(64.1) \qquad g(x) = x^2 - 2ax + a^2 - b.$$

As in the preceding section we have equation (63.1), whose coefficients are now known to be rational.   By the substitution

---

[1] The symbol $\sqrt{}$ will always be interpreted as meaning a fixed square root, which will be the positive value, when the root is real and not zero.

$x = a + \sqrt{b}$ we get

$$ca + c\sqrt{b} + d = 0,$$

whence $c = 0$, since that is the only way for $c\sqrt{b}$ to be rational. As before, $f(x)$ has both roots of $g(x)$ because the remainder is zero.

Theorem 64.1.—*In an equation with rational coefficients, quadratic surd roots occur in conjugate pairs.*

It is to be noted that the foregoing proof only assumes that the coefficients of the equation are taken from a field $\mathfrak{F}$ which contains a, b but not $\sqrt{b}$. For the coefficients of (64.1), and consequently those of the quotient and the remainder, are in $\mathfrak{F}$. Hence we have the following more general result which contains both Theorems 63.1 and 64.1.

Theorem 64.2.—*If an equation with coefficients in a field $\mathfrak{F}$ has a root $a + \sqrt{b}$, where a, b belong to $\mathfrak{F}$ but $\sqrt{b}$ does not, it also has the root $a - \sqrt{b}$.*

To illustrate the applications of this last theorem, suppose an equation with rational coefficients has a root $\sqrt{2} + \sqrt{3}$. Let the reader verify that the totality of numbers $a + b\sqrt{c}$ forms a field if a, b vary over a field $\mathfrak{F}$, c is a *fixed* member of $\mathfrak{F}$ and $\sqrt{c}$ does not belong to $\mathfrak{F}$. This field will be called the *extension of $\mathfrak{F}$ obtained by adjoining $\sqrt{c}$ to it* and will be denoted by $\mathfrak{F}(\sqrt{c})$. Of course, if c is divisible by a perfect square in $\mathfrak{F}$, that factor can be omitted in indicating the extension. Thus $\mathfrak{F}(\sqrt{a^2 c}) = \mathfrak{F}(\sqrt{c})$, if a belongs to $\mathfrak{F}$.

The equation under consideration has coefficients in $\mathfrak{R}(\sqrt{2})$. Let the reader verify that $\sqrt{3}$ does not belong to $\mathfrak{R}(\sqrt{2})$. By Theorem 64.2 the equation has the root $\sqrt{2} - \sqrt{3}$ also. Similarly, by considering $\mathfrak{R}(\sqrt{3})$ and the root $\sqrt{2} + \sqrt{3}$, the root $-\sqrt{2} + \sqrt{3}$ is seen to be present. Finally, by considering $\mathfrak{R}(\sqrt{2})$ and the root $-\sqrt{2} + \sqrt{3}$, the root $-\sqrt{2} - \sqrt{3}$ is seen to be present. Hence, any equation with rational coefficients having one of the numbers

$$\sqrt{2} + \sqrt{3}, \quad \sqrt{2} - \sqrt{3}, \quad -\sqrt{2} + \sqrt{3}, \quad -\sqrt{2} - \sqrt{3}$$

as a root has all the others. The equation of lowest degree having one of them as a root is accordingly

$$x^4 - 10x^2 + 1 = 0.$$

65. Transformation of Equations.—If we write

$$(65.1) \qquad y = kx, \qquad x = \frac{1}{k}y, \qquad k \neq 0,$$

the polynomial $f(x)$ becomes $f(y/k)$, a polynomial of the same degree in y, which will be denoted by $\varphi(y)$. If r is a root of $f(x) = 0$, then $f(r) = 0$. Since $f(r) = f(kr/k) = \varphi(kr)$, the equation $\varphi(y) = 0$ has the root $y = kr$. Consequently, the roots of f become those of φ when multiplied by k and the roots of φ become those of f when divided by k.

φ can be obtained from f by making the direct substitution $x = y/k$ or by employing the elementary symmetric polynomials. Let us apply the latter method to the equation

$$ax^3 + bx^2 + cx + d = 0.$$

Multiplying each root by k multiplies the sum by k, the sum of the products two at a time by k^2, the product of the three roots by k^3. Hence the elementary symmetric polynomials for the equation in y are

$$-\frac{kb}{a}, \qquad +\frac{k^2c}{a}, \qquad -\frac{k^3d}{a},$$

and the equation is after multiplication by a

$$ay^3 + kby^2 + k^2cy + k^3d = 0.$$

In particular, if we make $k = a$, the above elementary symmetric polynomials reduce to $-b$, ac, $-a^2d$, so that the result is

(65.2) $y^3 + by^2 + acy + a^2d = 0,$

an equation whose initial is 1. This transformation is useful at times in finding the rational roots of an equation with integral coefficients. After transformation, the rational roots are integral by Theorem 62.1.

Instead of multiplying all the roots by a number, we may increase them by the same number. This process corresponds to the formulas of transformation

(65.3) $y = x + k,$ $x = y - k.$

The sum of the roots will obviously be increased by nk under this operation, but how the other elementary symmetric polynomials are modified is not so obvious. A ready means of finding them will now be indicated.

Let the polynomial in y be

$$\varphi(y) = b_0 y^n + b_1 y^{n-1} + \cdots + b_n.$$

When y is replaced by $x + k$, this becomes identically equal to $f(x)$. Hence

$$f(x) = b_0(x + k)^n + b_1(x + k)^{n-1} + \cdots + b_{n-1}(x + k) + b_n.$$

From this it is clear that b_n is the remainder when $f(x)$ is divided by $x + k$; b_{n-1} is the remainder when the quotient of that division is divided by $x + k$; and so on.

The numerical determination of the coefficients is most readily accomplished by synthetic division. For this reason, it is convenient to regard the process as *diminishing* the roots by $-k$, rather than increasing them by $+k$. *The synthetic divisor is then precisely the quantity by which the roots are being diminished.*

If $f(x) = 3x^4 + 2x^2 + 5x - 1$ and the roots are to be diminished by 2, the numerical calculations are arranged as shown below.

$$
\begin{array}{rrrrr|r}
3 & +\,0 & +\,2 & +\,5 & -\,1 & 2 \\
  & +\,6 & +12 & +28 & +66 & \\
\hline
3 & +\,6 & +14 & +33 & +65 & \\
  & +\,6 & +24 & +76 & & \\
\hline
3 & +12 & +38 & +109 & & \\
  & +\,6 & +36 & & & \\
\hline
3 & +18 & +74 & & & \\
  & +\,6 & & & & \\
\hline
3 & +24 & & & & \\
\end{array}
$$

The new polynomial is

$$3y^4 + 24y^3 + 74y^2 + 109y + 65.$$

An important application of the second transformation is in making the coefficient of y^{n-1} equal to zero. If each root is diminished by $-\dfrac{a_1}{na_0}$, the sum is diminished by $-\dfrac{a_1}{a_0}$ and therefore becomes zero in the transformed equation. Fractions may be avoided by first multiplying the roots by na_0/b, where b is the highest common factor of a_1 and na_0.

EXERCISES

65.1–65.5. Transform the equations of Exercises 62 into equations with initial equal to 1.

By transformation, remove the second term from the following equations:

65.6. $2x^3 + 3x^2 - x + 1 = 0.$
65.7. $3x^4 - 8x^3 + 4x^2 - 2x + 1 = 0.$

66. Solution of the Quadratic.—The transformations of the preceding section are useful in solving the general quadratic equation

(66.1) $f(x) = ax^2 + bx + c = 0.$

First we multiply the roots by $2a$, and find

$$\varphi(y) = y^2 + 2by + 4ac = 0.$$

(The a is used to make the initial 1, the 2 in order to facilitate division by 2.) The sum of the roots is now $-2b$. If we diminish each root by $-b$, the sum will be decreased by $-2b$ and the new sum will be zero. We need only compute the constant term. Since it is the remainder when $\varphi(y)$ is divided by $y + b$, it is by the remainder theorem

$$\varphi(-b) = 4ac - b^2.$$

The transformed equation is accordingly

$$z^2 + 4ac - b^2 = 0.$$

It is solved by extracting the square root:

$$z = \pm\sqrt{b^2 - 4ac}.$$

Reversing our transformations, we obtain y by increasing by $-b$:

$$y = -b \pm \sqrt{b^2 - 4ac};$$

and x by dividing by $2a$:

(66.2) $$x = \frac{-b \pm \sqrt{b^2 - 4ac}}{2a}.$$

The expression under the radical is what will later be defined as the *discriminant*

(66.3) $$D = b^2 - 4ac.$$

Clearly we have

THEOREM 66.1.—*The roots of a quadratic polynomial with real coefficients are real and unequal, real and equal, or conjugate imaginary according as the discriminant is positive, zero, or negative.*

EXERCISES

66.1. If x_1, x_2 are the roots of (66.1), prove that $D = a^2(x_1 - x_2)^2$.

66.2. If a, b, c, x are real, the polynomial $ax^2 + bx + c$ has the same sign as a except when the roots are real and x lies between them. In the exceptional case, the polynomial has sign opposite to that of a.

66.3. Discuss the graph of a quadratic polynomial. Apply the results to Exercise 66.2.

66.4. Discuss the factorization of $ax^2 + bxy + cy^2$.

66.5. If a, b, c are rational, the roots of the quadratic are rational if and only if the discriminant is the square of a rational number.

66.6. If a, b, c are integers, the roots of the quadratic are integers if and only if b and c are divisible by a and the discriminant is the square of an integer.

66.7. Find a necessary and sufficient condition that

$$ax^2 + by^2 + cz^2 + 2fyz + 2gzx + 2hxy$$

be reducible for all values of y and z by considering it as a quadratic in the indeterminate x.

67. Solution of the Cubic.

—As before, we multiply the roots of

$$(67.1) \qquad f(x) = ax^3 + bx^2 + cx + d = 0$$

by $3a$, and obtain

$$\varphi(y) = y^3 + 3by^2 + 9acy + 27a^2d = 0.$$

The sum of the three roots is now $-3b$. Hence each is to be diminished by $-b$. The result is

$$(67.2) \qquad z^3 + pz + q = 0,$$

where

$$p = 9ac - 3b^2, \qquad q = 2b^3 - 9abc + 27a^2d.$$

It will be called the *reduced cubic*. To it we apply the further transformation

$$(67.3) \qquad z = t - \frac{p}{3t},$$

which gives on multiplication by t^3

(67.4) $$t^6 + qt^3 - \frac{p^3}{27} = 0.$$

This is a quadratic in t^3, so that the formula of the last section can be used to determine two values T, U for t^3. Let t be a definite cube root of T. The other two cube roots of T are ωt and $\omega^2 t$, where ω is an imaginary cube root of unity. From (67.3) we accordingly get as three roots of (67.2)

$$t - \frac{p}{3t}, \qquad \omega t - \frac{p\omega^2}{3t}, \qquad \omega^2 t - \frac{p\omega}{3t}.$$

If we put $u = -\dfrac{p}{3t}$, these become

(67.5) $$t + u, \qquad t\omega + u\omega^2, \qquad t\omega^2 + u\omega.$$

Since $t^3 u^3$ is minus the constant term of (67.4), we see that $u^3 = U$, that is, u^3 is the second root of (67.4). It is accordingly convenient to note that

(67.6) $$t^3 + u^3 = -q, \qquad t^3 u^3 = -\tfrac{1}{27}p^3.$$

Had we chosen u instead of t at the outset, we should have obtained for the roots

$$u - \frac{p}{3u}, \qquad u\omega - \frac{p\omega^2}{3u}, \qquad u\omega^2 - \frac{p\omega}{3u},$$

that is,

$$t + u, \qquad t\omega^2 + u\omega, \qquad t\omega + u\omega^2,$$

which are the same as (67.5) except for the order in which they are written. Similar results follow if ωt, $\omega^2 t$, ωu, or $\omega^2 u$ is used instead of t initially.

Increasing (67.5) by $-b$ and then dividing by $3a$ give the three roots of the original equation.

This method of solving the cubic is essentially the first ever given. It was discovered by del Ferro or by Tartaglia, but was first published by Cardan (1545).

EXERCISES

Apply the general method of this section to the transformation and solution of the following cubics.

67.1. $x^3 + 6x^2 + 18x + 13$.

67.2. $x^3 - 9x^2 + 9x - 8$.

67.3. $x^3 - 3x^2 - 3x - 1$.

67.4. $8x^3 + 24x^2 + 36x + 27$.

67.5. $x^3 + 9x^2 + 15x - 25$.

67.6. Factor $a^3 + b^3 + c^3 - 3abc$ by considering it as a cubic in the indeterminate a.

68. Cubics with Real Coefficients.—Consider now the case of *real coefficients*.

If the roots T, U of (67.4) are real, the real cube root of T will serve as t in the above discussion and the roots of the cubic are easily obtained. The discriminant of the quadratic (67.4) is, except for a positive factor,

$$(68.1) \qquad\qquad 4p^3 + 27q^2.$$

Hence, when this is positive, the roots of the cubic can be obtained in the form (67.5) by the extraction of the real cube root of a real number. Since t, u are real, the first of (67.5) is real and the other two are conjugate imaginary. In the case under consideration, therefore, the cubic has one real and two conjugate imaginary roots.

If (68.1) is zero, the roots of (67.4) are both equal to $-\frac{1}{2}q$. Since $t^3 = u^3$ and t, u are real, t/u is the real cube root of unity, that is, $t = u$. By use of (49.2) the values (67.5) become $2t$, $-t$, $-t$, or from the first of (67.6) we may take them as

$$(68.2) \qquad\qquad -\sqrt[3]{4q}, \qquad \sqrt[3]{\tfrac{1}{2}q}, \qquad \sqrt[3]{\tfrac{1}{2}q},$$

the radical indicating the real root. Thus the cubic (67.2) has two equal real roots.

If (68.1) is negative, p must be negative. This is called the *irreducible case* (see Sec. 70 for the significance of this term, which has nothing to do with irreducible polynomials). From the definition of u the product tu is necessarily positive. Hence we may write $t = re^{i\theta}$, $u = se^{-i\theta}$. From (67.6) the sum $t^3 + u^3 = r^3e^{3i\theta} + s^3e^{-3i\theta}$ is real and must therefore be equal to its conjugate $r^3e^{-3i\theta} + s^3e^{3i\theta}$. This requires that $r = s$, and t, u are *conjugate imaginary*. Hence all the roots (67.5) are real. They can be proved distinct as follows. If the first two are equal, it readily follows that $t = \omega^2 u$. The cubes of t and u are equal. Hence (67.4) has equal roots, so that (68.1) is zero, contrary to hypothesis. A similar result holds if any other two are equal.

The discriminant of the cubic (67.2) will be defined in Chapter XI and will turn out to be the negative of (68.1). We therefore adopt the following temporary definition of the discriminant

(68.3) $$D = -4p^3 - 27q^2.$$

(Note that the discriminants of the reduced cubic and the quadratic on which its solution depends differ by a *negative factor*.)   We evidently have

Theorem 68.1.—*A cubic with real coefficients has three real distinct roots, three real roots of which at least two are equal, or one real and two conjugate imaginary roots according as its discriminant is positive, zero, or negative.*

In applying this theorem and in making the computations of Sec. 69 it is convenient to use the formula

$$\frac{D}{108} = \left(-\frac{1}{3}p\right)^3 - \left(\frac{1}{2}q\right)^2.$$

EXERCISES

Calculate the discriminants of the reduced cubics and state the nature of the roots of each of the following.

68.1. $x^3 + 6x^2 + 6x - 2$.

68.2. $x^3 - 6x^2 + 3x + 20$.

68.3. $2x^3 + 12x^2 + 18x + 7$.

68.4. $x^3 - 3x^2 - x - 1$.

68.5. $4x^3 + 12x^2 - 15x + 4$.

69. Irreducible Case of the Cubic Treated by Trigonometry. In the case of positive discriminant, although the roots are real, their expressions (67.5) involve the cube roots of imaginary quantities. A method of transforming (67.5) so that they involve only real quantities in this case seems desirable.

One way of accomplishing this is by trigonometry. The roots of (67.4) can be written

$$(69.1) \qquad -\frac{q}{2} \pm \sqrt{\frac{-D}{108}}.$$

The representative point in the Argand diagram for the upper sign is

$$\left(-\frac{q}{2}, \sqrt{\frac{D}{108}}\right)$$

since D is positive. The distance of this point from the origin is

$$r = \sqrt{\frac{q^2}{4} + \frac{D}{108}} = \sqrt{-\frac{p^3}{27}}.$$

The amplitude, which is in the first or second quadrant according as q is negative or positive, is computed from

$$\tan \theta = -\sqrt{\frac{D}{108}} \div \frac{q}{2}.$$

By De Moivre's theorem the cube of

(69.2) $r^{\frac{1}{3}}(\cos \frac{1}{3}\theta + i \sin \frac{1}{3}\theta)$

is $r(\cos \theta + i \sin \theta)$. Hence (69.2) is one cube root of (69.1) and it will serve for t. Since u is conjugate to t,

$$u = r^{\frac{1}{3}}(\cos \frac{1}{3}\theta - i \sin \frac{1}{3}\theta).$$

Another cube root is $120° = \frac{2}{3}\pi$ farther around the circle. Hence the values of $t\omega$, $u\omega^2$, $t\omega^2$, $u\omega$ are obtained by increasing $\frac{1}{3}\theta$ by $\frac{2}{3}\pi$ and by $\frac{4}{3}\pi$. The three roots of the reduced cubic are accordingly

(69.3)
$$2\sqrt{-\frac{p}{3}} \cos \frac{1}{3}\theta, \qquad 2\sqrt{-\frac{p}{3}} \cos \frac{1}{3}(\theta + 2\pi),$$
$$2\sqrt{-\frac{p}{3}} \cos \frac{1}{3}(\theta + 4\pi).$$

Although formulas (69.3) were deduced for the irreducible case ($D > 0$, $p < 0$), they give the roots in all cases, as a little reflection shows they must.[1] They can be adapted to numerical computation in the case of real coefficients and negative discriminant by using hyperbolic functions.

If D and p are negative, $\tan \theta$ is pure imaginary with modulus less than unity, so that the equation $\tan \theta = i \tanh \varphi$ has the real solution $\varphi = \theta/i$, whose value can be found from

$$\tanh \varphi = -\sqrt{-D/108} \div \tfrac{1}{2}q$$

---

[1] V. Riccati, *Opusculorum ad res Physicas, et Mathematicas pertinentium*, vol. 1, Bologna, 1757, pp. 54, 77–80. W. D. Lambert, *A generalized trigonometric solution of the cubic equation*, American Mathematical Monthly, vol. 13 (1906), pp. 73–76. The usefulness of the hyperbolic functions in this connection was brought to the author's attention by W. T. Short. *Cf.* his paper *Hyperbolic solution of the cubic equation*, National Mathematics Magazine, vol. 12 (1937), pp. 111–114.

by means of tables.   From the addition formula of trigonometry we have

$$\cos \tfrac{1}{3}(\theta + k\pi) = \cos \tfrac{1}{3}k\pi \cosh \tfrac{1}{3}\varphi - i \sin \tfrac{1}{3}k\pi \sinh \tfrac{1}{3}\varphi.$$

The three roots are found by making $k = 0, 2, 4$ and multiplying by $2\sqrt{-p/3}$.

Since the radical in the expression for $\tan \theta$ is imaginary,
it may not be clear which of the two values $+i\sqrt{-D/108}$
or $-i\sqrt{-D/108}$ should be taken.   The first of these was
employed in the above computations.   The reader should note
the effect which choosing the other value has on φ and on the
roots.

Formulas for the case $p > 0$ can be obtained in similar
fashion.   Compute φ from

$$\tanh \varphi = -\tfrac{1}{2}q \div \sqrt{-D/108},$$

and replace θ by $\theta - \tfrac{1}{2}\pi$ to compensate for the inversion.   The
cosines are

$$\cos \tfrac{1}{3}(k + \tfrac{1}{2})\pi \cosh \tfrac{1}{3}\varphi - i \sin \tfrac{1}{3}(k + \tfrac{1}{2})\pi \sinh \tfrac{1}{3}\varphi.$$

These values are to be multiplied by $-2i\sqrt{p/3}$, the sign
having been chosen so that the real root $(k = 4)$ has opposite
sign to q.

In performing numerical work, it may be preferable to
determine φ from its hyperbolic sine or cosine which vary
over an infinite interval, whereas the tangent varies between
-1 and 1.   The calculations can be readily effected by using
the logarithms of the hyperbolic functions given in the Smith-
sonian Tables.[1]

EXERCISES

69.1–69.3. Determine which of Exercises 68 belong to the irreducible
case.   Find their roots correct to three decimals by means of logarithms.

[1] G. F. Becker and C. E. van Orstrand, *Hyperbolic Functions*, Wash-
ington, 1909.

Check the answers by forming the sum *and* the product of the roots. (The sum alone would not reveal an error in θ.)

70. Algebraic Discussion of the Irreducible Case.—Formulas (69.3) are real expressions for the roots, which are easily adapted to numerical calculation. They give the roots, however, as trigonometric functions. It is natural to inquire whether the roots cannot always be expressed by a finite number of real radicals. That the answer is in the negative follows from

Theorem 70.1.—*A cubic equation which is irreducible in the rational field, and which has three real (and distinct) roots, does not have any root expressible in terms of a finite number of real radicals.*

Let f be a cubic with rational coefficients and three real, irrational roots. Suppose one of its roots can be compounded from rational numbers by a finite number of real root extractions. Let $\mathfrak{F}$ be the field obtained by adjoining to the rational field all but one of the radicals, say α, necessary for expressing the root, that is, suppose f is irreducible in $\mathfrak{F}$ but reducible in $\mathfrak{F}(\alpha)$, the field obtained by adjoining α to $\mathfrak{F}$. The order of the radical α can be assumed prime: if its order is mn, for example, we can adjoin the mth root and subsequently the nth root of it.

Let α be a root of

$$\varphi(x) = x^p - a,$$

where a is in $\mathfrak{F}$ and is not a perfect pth power of a quantity in $\mathfrak{F}$. Then (Sec. 59) φ is irreducible in $\mathfrak{F}$.

Any symbol of $\mathfrak{F}(\alpha)$ is of the form

(70.1)
$$\frac{r(\alpha)}{s(\alpha)},$$

where r, s are polynomials with coefficients in $\mathfrak{F}$, and $s(x)$ is not divisible by $\varphi(x)$. Since φ is irreducible, φ and s are relatively prime. Hence we can find by Euclid's division algorithm polynomials $P(x)$, $Q(x)$ with coefficients in $\mathfrak{F}$ satisfying

$$s(x)P(x) + \varphi(x)Q(x) = 1.$$

Substitution of α gives

$$s(\alpha)P(\alpha) = 1,$$

so that (70.1) becomes $r(\alpha)P(\alpha)$, that is, a polynomial in α. By use of $\alpha^p = a$, the degree of this polynomial can be made less than p. Hence, $\mathfrak{F}(\alpha)$ *consists of all polynomials in α of degree less than p with coefficients in $\mathfrak{F}$* (and the polynomial zero).

Now f is reducible in $\mathfrak{F}(\alpha)$, so that we may write

(70.2) $$f(x) = g(x, \alpha)h(x, \alpha),$$

where g, h are polynomials (in two indeterminates, see Sec. 79) with coefficients in $\mathfrak{F}$. Let the other roots of φ be $\alpha_1, \cdots,$ α_{p-1}. For fixed x from $\mathfrak{F}$, consider the equation

$$f(x) - g(x, y)h(x, y) = 0.$$

Because of (70.2) it has a root α in common with the irreducible equation $\varphi(y) = 0$ and hence all the α's satisfy it. Replacing α by $\alpha_1, \cdots, \alpha_{p-1}$ in (70.2) and multiplying the resulting equations give

(70.3) $f(x)^p = g(x, \alpha)g(x, \alpha_1) \cdots g(x, \alpha_{p-1})h(x, \alpha)h(x, \alpha_1)$
$$\cdots h(x, \alpha_{p-1}).$$

The product of the g's is a symmetric polynomial in the α's. Hence, as we shall see in Sec. 83, it is a polynomial in the elementary symmetric polynomials of φ, which belong to $\mathfrak{F}$. Similarly for the h's. Hence we have

(70.4) $$f(x)^p = G(x)H(x),$$

where the coefficients of G, H belong to $\mathfrak{F}$. Since f is irreducible, G and H can be written

(70.5) $$G = f^{p_1}, \qquad H = f^{p_2},$$

where

$$p_1 + p_2 = p.$$

Hence the degrees of G, H are $3p_1$, $3p_2$. But from the right member of (70.3) we see that these degrees are divisible by p. Since neither p_1 nor p_2 can be divisible by p, it follows that $p = 3$.

We may therefore write the root of f under consideration as

(70.6) $$x = b + c\alpha + d\alpha^2.$$

Consider the expressions obtained by replacing α by the other roots of φ, namely, $\alpha\omega$, $\alpha\omega^2$:

(70.7) $$x = b + c\alpha\omega + d\alpha^2\omega^2, \qquad x = b + c\alpha\omega^2 + d\alpha^2\omega.$$

If these three equations are transposed to the left and multiplied together, a polynomial F of degree 3 results, whose coefficients are symmetric in the three roots of φ and therefore (Sec. 83) belong to $\mathfrak{F}$. As the polynomial F has the root (70.6) in common with irreducible f, the two polynomials have exactly the same roots. Hence (70.7) are real. Substituting $\omega^2 = -\omega - 1$ and putting the coefficient of ω equal to zero give $c\alpha = d\alpha^2$. Now $c = d = 0$ would mean f had a root in $\mathfrak{F}$, contrary to assumption. Hence $\alpha = c/d$, and α is contained in $\mathfrak{F}$, likewise contrary to assumption. This contradiction proves the theorem.[1]

The case of positive discriminant is accordingly called the *irreducible case*. See the problem in the next section.

71. Solution of the Quartic.—First multiply the roots of

(71.1) $$ax^4 + bx^3 + cx^2 + dx + e = 0$$

---

[1] The proof just given was inspired by that in Weber-Wellstein, *Enzyklopädie der Elementarmathematik*, 4th ed., vol. 1, pp. 436–437.

by a and obtain[1]

$$(71.2) \qquad y^4 + by^3 + acy^2 + a^2dy + a^3e = 0.$$

Next diminish the roots by $-\frac{1}{4}b$, obtaining

$$(71.3) \qquad z^4 + Qz^2 + Rz + S = 0.$$

The left member is the product of two quadratic factors, with initials equal to unity. The sum of the two coefficients of z in these factors is the negative sum of all four roots of (71.3). Hence it is zero, and the two factors can be assumed in the form

$$(71.4) \qquad (z^2 - kz + l)(z^2 + kz + m).$$

Identification of the coefficients with those in (71.3) gives

$$(71.5) \quad l + m = k^2 + Q, \qquad k(l - m) = R, \qquad lm = S.$$

Multiply the first of these by k, square, and subtract from it the square of the second. Finally, substitute the value of $4k^2lm$ given by the last. In this way, l, m are eliminated to give

$$(71.6) \qquad k^6 + 2Qk^4 + (Q^2 - 4S)k^2 - R^2 = 0.$$

This is an equation of the third degree in k^2. It will be called the *resolvent cubic*. Its three roots will be denoted by $4A^2$, $4B^2$, $4C^2$. By inspection of the equation (71.6) the product $64A^2B^2C^2$ is R^2. Let us fix the meaning of A, B, C, whose signs may be changed at pleasure, so that $R = -8ABC$. Similarly, by inspection, $Q = -2(A^2 + B^2 + C^2)$. Substituting these values and $k = 2A \neq 0$ in (71.5) gives

---

[1] In examples with integral coefficients, other ways of proceeding from (71.1) to (71.3) will occur to the reader. If b is not divisible by 4, it is well to make the second coefficient so divisible by multiplying the roots by the suitable number. If b is divisible by $4a$ as in Exercise 71.2, it is convenient to diminish the roots by $-b/(4a)$ at once.

$$l + m = 2(A^2 - B^2 - C^2), \qquad l - m = -4BC,$$

whence

$$l = (A + B + C)(A - B - C),$$
$$m = (-A + B - C)(-A - B + C).$$

Since the sum of the two factors of l is $2A = k$, these two factors are the roots of the first factor of (71.4); and similarly the two factors of m are the roots of the second factor of (71.4). Hence the four roots of the original quartic are

$$(71.7) \qquad A + B + C, \qquad A - B - C, \qquad -A + B - C,$$
$$-A - B + C.$$

The above discussion has been based upon the existence of a non-zero root of (71.6). If all the roots of (71.6) are zero, however, then $Q = R = S = 0$ and all the roots of (71.3) are zero, so that (71.7) give the roots in all cases.

This method of solving the quartic is Descartes', but the answer has been thrown in the form given by Euler. The first solution was given by Ferrari (cf. Exercise 71.6, below).

The method can be applied to the discussion of the so-called Spanish student's problem: to solve

$$x^2 + y = 7, \qquad x + y^2 = 11.$$

Solving the first equation for y and substituting in the second give

$$x^4 - 14x^2 + x + 38 = 0.$$

This equation has the rational root 2. The depressed equation

$$x^3 + 2x^2 - 10x - 19 = 0$$

has no rational root and has positive discriminant. Hence the k^2 in (71.4) cannot be expressed by real radicals, and the resolvent cubic (71.6)

$$k^6 - 28k^4 + 44k^2 - 1 = 0$$

cannot be solved by real radicals.

Although the problem has the solution $x = 2$, $y = 3$, Descartes' method will not give a solution in that form because the irreducible case of the cubic is encountered.

EXERCISES

Apply the general method of reduction and solution to the following quartics. In these particular problems, whenever the resolvent cubic has positive discriminant, it has at least one rational root, which should be found by trial.

71.1. $x^4 + 4x^3 - 9x^2 - 16x + 20.$

71.2. $16x^4 + 64x^3 + 120x^2 + 48x - 63.$

71.3. $x^4 - 4x^3 + 9x^2 - 4x + 8.$

71.4. $4x^4 + 16x^3 - 8x^2 - 64x + 19.$

71.5. $4x^4 - 16x^3 + 12x^2 - 12x - 9.$

71.6. Write (71.2) in the form

$$(y^2 + \tfrac{1}{2}by)^2 = (\tfrac{1}{4}b^2 - ac)y^2 - a^2dy - a^3e,$$

add $(y^2 + \tfrac{1}{2}b)k + \tfrac{1}{4}k^2$ to each member and express that the right member be the square of a polynomial linear in y. A cubic in k is obtained. Show how it can be employed to solve the quartic.

71.7. Apply the method (Ferrari's) of Exercise 71.6 to the polynomial $x^4 + 4x^3 + 7x^2 + 10x + 3.$

71.8. Find the conditions that the left member of (71.1) be the square of a quadratic polynomial.

71.9. Find the conditions that the left member of (71.1) be the fourth power of a linear polynomial.

71.10. Changing the sign of two of the letters A, B, C leaves the relation $R = -8ABC$ unaltered. What is the effect on the roots (71.7)?

72. Equations of Higher Degree.—In the preceding sections we have given algebraic methods for solving the general equations (that is, equations with indeterminates for coefficients) of degrees 2, 3, and 4. The methods, of course, will serve to solve any equation with numerical coefficients whose degree does not exceed 4.

When the degree exceeds 4, however, not only does the general equation fail to admit solution by algebraic methods, but an equation with numerical coefficients does also except when it belongs to a special category called *solvable*. The proof of these facts, together with methods for determining when a given equation is solvable, belongs to the Galois theory of equations.

Even when the degree does not exceed 4, the methods of solution, while entirely. satisfactory from the theoretical standpoint, may not be very convenient to apply to numerical examples.

For these reasons, it is desirable to develop for equations of arbitrary degree methods of locating the roots and approximating them to any desired accuracy.

73. Location of Roots.—We shall treat only the case of real roots of equations with real coefficients. All others can be reduced to it in the following way. If the unknown is assumed to be complex $x + iy$, substitution in the equation and separation of real from imaginary give two equations with real coefficients in the real unknowns x, y. As we shall see later (Chapter XII), any particular solution of these two equations can be found by obtaining a solution of two equations each in a *single* unknown.

A result useful in locating real roots is

Theorem 73.1.—*If $f(x)$ is a polynomial with real coefficients, if a and b are real numbers and if $f(a), f(b)$ have opposite signs, there is at least one real root of $f(x) = 0$ between a and b. The sign of f is the same at all numbers between two consecutive real roots.*

To prove the theorem, we may suppose $a < b$ and $f(b) > 0$, for if $f(b) < 0$, we may consider $-f(x) = 0$, which has the same roots as $f(x) = 0$.

The proof is accomplished by use of the axiom of continuity (Sec. 1). The separation of the real numbers into two classes is done in the following way. The real number y is placed in the class R if $y \geq b$, or if $y < b$ and $f(x)$ is positive for every number x on the interval $y \leq x \leq b$. On the other hand, y is placed in L if $y < b$ and $f(x)$ is zero or negative for at least one value of x on $y \leq x \leq b$.

The above rule tells how to place every real number in one and only one of the two classes. Clearly, a belongs to L and b to R. Hence (i) and (ii) of the axiom of continuity are satisfied. To see that (iii) is also satisfied, let z belong to L and satisfy $y \leq z \leq b$, where y belongs to R. Since $f(x)$ is positive on the whole interval $y \leq x \leq b$, it is also positive on the subinterval $z \leq x \leq b$. Hence z belongs to R. As this is a contradiction, (iii) is satisfied.

Let c be the separating number whose existence is stated by the axiom. Every point x satisfying $x < c$ belongs to L, and every point x satisfying $c < x$ belongs to R. If δ is positive, then $f(x)$ is positive somewhere on $c < x < c + \delta$. Since $c - \delta$ belongs to L, $f(x)$ is zero or negative at some point on $c - \delta \leq x \leq b$ and consequently at some point on $c - \delta \leq x \leq c + \delta$. Hence $f(x)$ changes sign on $c - \delta \leq x \leq c + \delta$.

Suppose $f(c) \neq 0$. Theorem 46.1 applied to the 0-fold root c shows that $f(c)f(x) > 0$ on $c - \delta \leq x \leq c + \delta$ for δ sufficiently small. This is a contradiction, however, for $f(x)$ has been seen to change sign on that interval.

The hypothesis $f(c) \neq 0$ being untenable, $f(c) = 0$ and the theorem is proved.

The theorem, of course, is rather obvious from the graphical representation. Moreover, it is also clear from the graph that the hypothesis is not a necessary condition: $f(a)$ and $f(b)$ may have the same sign when there is a root between a and b.

To generalize the theorem slightly, we suppose that

$$f(x) = g(x)h(x),$$

where all the roots of g are real and lie between a and b, and where $h(x)$ has no roots between a and b. The sign of $h(x)$ is therefore the same at all values between a and b: if h changed sign, the theorem would show that h had a root on the interval.

Let

$$g(x) = (x - \alpha_1)(x - \alpha_2) \cdots (x - \alpha_k),$$

then in

$$g(a) = (a - \alpha_1)(a - \alpha_2) \cdots (a - \alpha_k)$$

all the factors are negative so that $g(a)$ has the same sign as $(-1)^k$. On the other hand, in

$$g(b) = (b - \alpha_1)(b - \alpha_2) \cdots (b - \alpha_k)$$

all the factors are positive, so that $g(b)$ is positive. Hence we have

THEOREM 73.2.—*If $f(a)f(b) \neq 0$, there is an even or an odd number of roots between a and b according as $f(a)$ and $f(b)$ have the same or opposite signs.*

Since 0 is an even number, $f(x)$ may have no roots between a and b when $f(a)$ and $f(b)$ have the same sign.

We shall write $f(\infty) = +$ to mean that $f(x)$ is positive for all positive values of x which are sufficiently large. Likewise we use sgn x to mean "the sign of x." We then have, when f is of even degree (*cf.* Sec. 47),

(73.1) $\quad f(-\infty) = \text{sgn } a_0, \quad f(0) = \text{sgn } a_n, \quad f(\infty) = \text{sgn } a_0,$

and, when f is of odd degree,

(73.2) $\quad f(-\infty) = -\text{sgn } a_0, \quad f(0) = \text{sgn } a_n, \quad f(\infty) = \text{sgn } a_0.$

If $a_n \neq 0$, (73.1) has no change of sign or two changes according as a_0 and a_n have the same or opposite signs. The sequence (73.2) always has a change of sign; in the case $a_n = 0$ the equation has the root zero.   We may state these results as

THEOREM 73.3.—*An equation of even degree with real coefficients has at least one positive and one negative root if its initial and constant term have opposite signs.*

An equation of odd degree with real coefficients has at least one real root, which is positive if the initial and constant term have opposite signs, negative if they have the same sign, and zero if the constant term vanishes.

Because of Theorem 73.1, to locate real roots, we may substitute real numbers synthetically until a change in sign is encountered.   By substituting numbers differing less and less we can locate the root with greater and greater precision.   For locating a root more closely than between consecutive integers however the method is usually tedious.

EXERCISES

73.1–73.10. Apply the method of this section to locate the real roots of the equations in Exercises 68.1 to 68.5, 71.1 to 71.5.

74. Relations between the Number of Real Roots of a Polynomial and Its Derivatives.

—All roots of f with multiplicity greater than 1 are roots of f'.   It will be convenient to call the other roots of f' *proper*.   In general, any root of $f^{(j)}$ which is not a root of $f^{(j-1)}$ will be called proper.

Theorem 46.2 gives the behavior of ff' except near a proper root of f'.   From the definitions in Sec. 46 we have

THEOREM 74.1.—*At a proper root of f' the polynomial ff' changes from plus to minus or vice versa according as the corresponding point is a hump or a depression.*

Next we prove (for polynomials)

ROLLE'S THEOREM 74.2.—*If a, b are consecutive roots of $f(x) = 0$, the derivative $f'(x)$ has an odd number of roots on $a < x < b$.*

The sign of f is the same at all points of $a < x < b$ by Theorem 73.1. Hence f' changes sign on the segment if and only if ff' does. By Theorem 46.2, however, ff' is plus just after the root a and negative just before b. If k, l are on the segment and are sufficiently close to a, b, respectively, $f'(k)$, $f'(l)$ have opposite signs and $f'(x)$ does not vanish on $a < x \leqq k$ or $l \leqq x < b$. The result therefore follows from Theorem 73.2 applied to f' on $l < x < k$.

Since the number of roots of f' on the segment is odd, at least one root has odd multiplicity. Hence there is at least one extremum of f between a and b. This result is also obvious from the graph.

Let N_{ab} denote the number of roots which f has on $a < x \leqq b$, that is, on a segment closed at its upper end[1] only. If $a < c < b$, we then have

$$N_{ac} + N_{cb} = N_{ab}.$$

Consequently, to obtain the value of N for a segment, we may divide the segment into parts and add the N's for the various pieces. For this reason, N_{ab} is called an *additive* function of the segment.

The notation $N_{ab}^{(j)}$ will mean the number of proper roots of $f^{(j)}$. Similarly, $H_{ab}^{(j)}$, $D_{ab}^{(j)}$ will denote the number of humps and depressions. These functions are likewise additive.

A sequence of real constants

(74.1) $y_1, \quad y_2, \quad \cdots, \quad y_l$

is said to *have V variations of sign* if the sign of its member changes V times as we read from left to right disregarding zeros. Thus the sequence

---

[1] This phrase will be abbreviated to "segment" in Sec. 74–76. A. Hurwitz, Mathematische Annalen, vol. 71 (1912), p. 584, seems the first to have proved a rigorous form of Budan's theorem for this type of point set.

$$3, \quad 0, \quad 4, \quad -1, \quad 0, \quad 5, \quad 2, \quad -2, \quad -3$$

has three variations of sign. If (74.1) has no zero members, except possibly the last, the number of its variations is the same as the number of minus signs in

$$(74.2) \qquad y_1 y_2, \qquad y_2 y_3, \qquad y_3 y_4, \qquad \cdots, \qquad y_{l-1} y_l.$$

The number of variations of sign in the sequence of derivatives of a polynomial f

$$(74.3) \qquad f, \qquad f', \qquad f'', \qquad \cdots, \qquad f^{(n)}$$

is of considerable importance. It depends on the value assigned x and will be denoted by V_x.

Choose c so near to b that the polynomial

$$(74.4) \qquad\qquad ff' \cdots f^{(n-1)}$$

has no root on $c \leq x < b$. Then $V_c = V_x$ for the same values. We display part of (74.3) as

$$(74.5) \quad f^{(j-1)}, \qquad f^{(j)}, \qquad \cdots, \qquad f^{(j+k-1)}, \qquad f^{(j+k)}.$$

If b is a proper k-fold root of $f^{(j)}$, the above becomes at b

$$(74.6) \quad f^{(j-1)}(b), \qquad 0, \qquad \cdots, \qquad 0, \qquad f^{(j+k)}(b).$$

By Theorem 46.2 the products

$$(74.7) \quad f^{(j)} f^{(j+1)}, \qquad f^{(j+1)} f^{(j+2)}, \qquad \cdots, \qquad f^{(j+k-1)} f^{(j+k)}$$

are all negative at c. Hence the last $k + 1$ members of (74.5) show k variations of sign, all of which are lost at b, as is seen from (74.6). If $j = 0$, this is the whole story, because $f^{(j-1)}$ does not exist. In this case, $N_{cb}^{(j)} = k$ variations of sign are lost in passing from c to b.

If $j > 0$, $f^{(j)}$ has a predecessor in (74.5). We now confine our attention to the first two members of (74.5) evaluated at c and write their product as

(74.8) $$f^{(j-1)}(c) \cdot f^{(j)}(c).$$

Similarly, the first and last members of (74.6) give

(74.9) $$f^{(j-1)}(b) \cdot f^{(j+k)}(b).$$

Since $f^{(j-1)}(c)f^{(j-1)}(b) > 0$, the products (74.8), (74.9) have the same or opposite sign according as

(74.10) $$f^{(j)}(c) \cdot f^{(j+k)}(b)$$

is positive or negative. Theorem 46.1 applied to $f^{(j)}$ shows that $f^{(j)}(c)$ and $(c - b)^k f^{(j+k)}(b)$ have the same sign if c is near enough to b. We suppose that c was originally chosen to satisfy this condition. Then, since $c - b$ is negative, product (74.10) has the sign of $(-1)^k$, that is, (74.8) and (74.9) have the same or opposite signs according as k is even or odd. In the first case, there is no change in variations in addition to the k originally counted. In the second case (k odd), a variation will be lost if (74.8) is negative and gained if (74.8) is positive. We may state this as: the *increase* is unity and has the sign of (74.8). But $f^{(j-1)}$ has a depression or hump (Sec. 46) according as (74.8) is negative or positive. Hence the net decrease in variations because of the proper zero of $f^{(j)}$ is

(74.11) $$N_{cb}^{(j)} + D_{cb}^{(j-1)} - H_{cb}^{(j-1)}.$$

This is to be summed for $j = 1, 2, \cdots, n$ and added to the N_{cb} obtained for $f^{(0)} = f$. From the additive property, moreover, we see that the result is true for any a, b. Hence the final formula is

(74.12) $$V_a - V_b = N_{ab} + \sum_{j=1}^{n} [N_{ab}^{(j)} + D_{ab}^{(j-1)} - H_{ab}^{(j-1)}].$$

We note that the D and H in (74.11) vanish unless the N is odd, and that when N is odd, one of them is unity and the other zero. Hence (74.11) is always even. It will also be noted that the only negative terms on the right of (74.12) are canceled by the corresponding N's. Hence, V *never increases as x increases.*

The result, known for $f(a)f(b) \neq 0$ as Budan's theorem, follows immediately from the above. It is

THEOREM 74.3.—*If $a < b$, then*

$$V_a - V_b = N_{ab} + 2k,$$

where k is a non-negative integer.

75. Descartes' rule of signs is given in

THEOREM 75.1.—*The number of positive roots of an equation with real coefficients is equal to the number of variations in sign of its coefficients*

$$(75.1) \qquad a_0, \qquad a_1, \qquad \cdots, \qquad a_n$$

diminished by a non-negative even integer.

To prove the theorem, apply (74.12) to 0, ∞. V_0 is the number of variations in (75.1) because the Taylor expansion shows that sequence (75.1) differs from the derivatives $f(0)$, $f'(0)$, $\cdots$, $f^{(n)}(0)$ only by positive factors. For $x = \infty$ sequence (74.3) has the signs of (Sec. 47)

$$a_0, \qquad a_0, \qquad \cdots, \qquad a_0$$

so that $V_\infty = 0$. The result therefore follows in the form

$$(75.2) \qquad V_0 = V_0 - V_\infty = N + 2k,$$

where k is non-negative.

If the roots of $f(x) = 0$ are multiplied (Sec. 65) by -1, the negative roots of $f(x)$ are transformed into the positive roots of $f(-x) = 0$, and an application of Descartes' rule to $f(-x)$

will give information about the negative roots of the original equation.

From (75.2) we conclude $N \leqq V_0$, that is,

Theorem 75.2.—*The number of positive roots does not exceed the number of variations of sign in the polynomial.*

A simple, direct proof of this form of Descartes' rule can be given by synthetic division.[1]

If V_0 is odd, we infer $1 \leqq N$. Aside from this, the rule never states the actual existence of any positive roots. Budan's theorem is subject to similar limitations.

Illustrative Examples.—(i) The polynomial

$$f(x) = x^4 + x^2 + x - 1$$

has one variation of sign. $f(-x)$ also has one variation. Hence Theorem 75.1 shows that there are exactly one positive root and exactly one negative root. The other two must be imaginary, and by Theorem 63.1 they are conjugates. In this case, Descartes' rule gives the exact nature of the roots.

(ii) The polynomial

$$f(x) = x^4 + 2x^3 + x^2 - 1$$

has one variation of sign and $f(-x)$ has three. Hence there are exactly one positive root and one or three negative roots. Descartes' rule does not give complete information. For the application of Budan's theorem we have

$$V_{-2} = 4, \qquad V_{-1} = 3, \qquad V_0 = 1.$$

Hence there is a root on $-2 < x \leqq -1$, and f has either no other negative roots or two negative roots on $-1 < x \leqq 0$. But on that segment

$$x^4 + 2x^3 \leqq 0, \qquad x^2 - 1 < 0,$$

so that f is negative and there is no root on $-1 < x \leqq 0$.

[1] H. B. Fine, *College Algebra*, p. 446.

EXERCISES

Apply Descartes' and Budan's theorems to each of the following polynomials. If the theorems do not give complete information, try to find the exact number of real roots by supplementary means.

75.1. $x^n - 1$, n odd. **75.2.** $x^n - 1$, n even.

75.3. $x^3 + x^2 + x + 1$. **75.4.** $x^3 - x^2 + x + 1$.

75.5–75.14. The polynomials in Exercises 68.1 to 68.5 and 71.1 to 71.5.

75.15. If the signs of the coefficients of the reduced cubic are $+++$, the cubic has exactly one real root, which is negative. If the signs are $++-$, there is exactly one real root, which is positive. What can be said of the cases $+-+$ and $++-$? Verify the results by using the discriminant (Theorem 68.1).

76. Sturm's Polynomials and Method.—Taken in conjunction with Budan's and Descartes' rules, the method of Sec. 73, although it only tells us whether the number of roots between a and b is even or odd, nevertheless locates the roots with sufficient precision for many purposes. At times, however, it is desirable to know *exactly* how many roots there are between a and b. Sturm's method, which will now be explained, furnishes this information.

Let f_0 be a polynomial with real coefficients and with simple roots, and let f_1 be its derivative. To f_0, f_1, we apply the method for finding the highest common factor (Sec. 35) by constructing a sequence like (3.1), of which f_0 and f_1 are the first members. We make, however, two modifications of the usual method. First, in avoiding fractions, the *modulus* of the divisor's initial is employed, rather than the initial itself, as in Sec. 30. Second, the remainder has its sign changed before being placed in the sequence. If the sequence is

$$(76.1) \qquad f_0, \qquad f_1, \qquad f_2, \qquad \cdots, \qquad f_l,$$

we have

$$(76.2) \quad c_0 f_0 = f_1 q_1 - f_2, \qquad c_1 f_1 = f_2 q_2 - f_3, \qquad \cdots,$$
$$c_{l-2} f_{l-2} = f_{l-1} q_{l-1} - f_l,$$

where the c's are positive constants and f_l is a non-zero constant, since f_0, f_1 are relatively prime (Sec. 35). (76.1) will be called *Sturm's sequence*.

STURM'S THEOREM 76.1.—*For a polynomial without multiple roots*

$$(76.3) \qquad N_{ab} = S_a - S_b,$$

where S_x denotes the number of variations of sign in Sturm's sequence.

To prove this result, we suppose that the polynomial

$$(76.4) \qquad f_0 f_1 \cdots f_l$$

has no root on $c \leqq x < b$. Then $S_c = S_x$. A change in the number of variations can only occur at a root of the product (76.4). Let $f_j(b) = 0$. Consider first the case $j > 0$. Then $f_{j-1}(b) f_{j+1}(b) \neq 0$: if $f_{j-1}(b)$ is zero, for example, both $f_{j-1}(x)$ and $f_j(x)$ have the factor $x - b$, and by the fundamental property of every sequence (3.1) $x - b$ divides f_0, f_1, which by hypothesis are without a common factor involving x. Moreover, we infer from (76.2)

$$(76.5) \qquad c_{j-1} f_{j-1}(b) = -f_{j+1}(b).$$

Since c_{j-1} is positive, the two end members of the subsequence

$$(76.6) \qquad f_{j-1}(c), \qquad f_j(c), \qquad f_{j+1}(c)$$

have opposite signs if c is near enough to b. We suppose c initially so chosen. Whatever the sign of $f_j(c)$, the sequence (76.6) has one variation and the same is true of the corresponding sequence for b:

$$f_{j-1}(b), \qquad 0, \qquad f_{j+1}(b).$$

Hence the subsequence

$$f_1, \qquad f_2, \qquad \cdots, \qquad f_l$$

has the same number of variations for b as for c.

If $j = 0$, there is no relation (76.5). We still have to consider, therefore, the effect of a root of f_0 on the variations in the sequence. Theorem 46.2 shows that $f_0 f_1$, which is zero for b, is negative for c. Hence (76.1) has one more variation for c than for b.

As a particular result, we have

THEOREM 76.2.—*The total number of real roots is*

$$S_{-\infty} - S_{\infty}.$$

Unlike Budan's and Descartes' theorems, the theorem of Sturm involves no undetermined integer. It tells the *exact* number of real roots between any two limits. From the theoretical standpoint, it is therefore completely satisfactory. The numerical computations involved in the determination of Sturm's sequence may, however, be so lengthy even for an equation of low degree as to render the method impractical.

Illustrative Example.

$$f_0 = x^3 - x^2 + x + 1, \qquad f_1 = 3x^2 - 2x + 1, \qquad f_2 = -2x - 5,$$
$$f_3 = -1.$$

$$
\begin{array}{rrrr|rrr}
9 & -9 & +9 & +9 & 3 & +2 & -1 \\
 & +6 & -3 & & & & \\
 & & -2 & +1 & & & \\
\hline
3 & -1 & 4 & +10 & & & \\
 & & 2 & +5 & & & \\
\end{array}
$$

$$
\begin{array}{rrr|rr}
12 & -8 & +4 & -2 & +5 \\
 & -30 & +95 & & \\
\hline
-6 & +19 & +99 & & \\
 & & +1 & & \\
\end{array}
$$

Multiply f_0 by $3^2 = 9$, since the initial of f_1 is 3. In the remainder of f_0/f_1, the common factor $+2$ can be omitted, so that the first remainder can be taken as $2x + 5$. Its negative is f_2, which is then divided into $4f_1$. The positive remainder 99 can be replaced by $+1$, so that $f_3 = -1$.

We then compute the table.

x	f_0	f_1	f_2	f_3	V
$-\infty$	$-$	$+$	$+$	$-$	2
∞	$+$	$+$	$-$	$-$	1
0	$+$	$+$	$-$	$-$	1
-1	$-$	$+$	$-$	$-$	2

Since $V_{-\infty} - V_{\infty} = 1$, there is only one real root. Since $V_{-\infty} - V_0 = 1$, that root is not positive. Since $V_{-1} - V_0 = 1$, it is on the segment $-1 < x \leqq 0$. We state the result as $[-1, 0]$.

Similarly, the notation $[1,2; 3,3\frac{1}{2}; 3\frac{1}{2},4]$ may be used to indicate that an equation has exactly three real roots lying respectively on the sets $1 < x \leqq 2; 3 < x \leqq 3\frac{1}{2}; 3\frac{1}{2} < x \leqq 4$.

EXERCISES

Find Sturm's polynomials and from them determine the number of real roots for each of the following polynomials. Locate each root on a segment $a < x \leqq a + 1$, where a is integral, and if two roots lie on such a segment, subdivide it so as to separate them.

76.1–76.5. The polynomials in Exercises 68.1–68.5.

76.6. $2x^3 + x^2 + 2x - 1$.

76.7. $3x^4 - 4x^3 + 6x^2 + 12x + 3$.

76.8. $x^4 - x^2 + 2x - 1$.

76.9. $7x^4 + 28x^3 + 34x^2 + 12x + 1$.

76.10. $112x^4 - 224x^3 + 136x^2 - 24x + 1$.

77. Approximation by a Linear Equation.

—If $0 < x < 1$, the square and higher powers of x may be numerically so small in the equation $f(x) = 0$ that the terms of higher degree than the first can be neglected and an approximation to x can be obtained from the linear equation

$$(77.1) \qquad a_{n-1}x + a_n = 0.$$

Thus, when $x = .1$, then $x^2 = .01$, $x^3 = .001$, and unless their coefficients are large, the terms in x^2, x^3 will be small in comparison with the others. This idea will now be rendered more precise.

Let us write

(77.2) $$f(x) = \varphi(x) + a_{n-1}x + a_n,$$

where φ denotes the aggregate of terms of degree higher than the first. If x is a root of $f(x) = 0$ and $a_{n-1} \neq 0$, then

(77.3) $$x + \frac{a_n}{a_{n-1}} = -\frac{\varphi(x)}{a_{n-1}}.$$

Since

$$\varphi(x) = a_0 x^n + \cdots + a_{n-2}x^2,$$

as in Sec. 45, we have

$$|\varphi(x)| \leq A(|x|^n + \cdots + |x|^2) = \frac{A(|x|^2 - |x|^{n+1})}{1 - |x|},$$

where A is the maximum modulus of the coefficients a_0, $\cdots$, a_{n-2} and where we have summed the geometric progression on the right by the usual formula. If $0 < |x| < 1$, we therefore have

$$|\varphi(x)| < \frac{A|x|^2}{1 - |x|}.$$

Use of this in (77.3) gives

(77.4) $$\left| x + \frac{a_n}{a_{n-1}} \right| < \frac{A|x|^2}{|a_{n-1}|(1 - |x|)} \leq \frac{AB^2}{|a_{n-1}|(1 - B)},$$

where B is known to satisfy $|x| \leq B < 1$. Naturally, the usefulness of this formula is conditioned by the readiness with which we can find a (small) B.

The root of (77.1), namely, $-\dfrac{a_n}{a_{n-1}}$, differs from the root x of $f(x)$ by less than the right member of (77.4).

If $a_{n-k} \neq 0$, $a_{n-k+1} = \cdots = a_{n-1} = 0$, replace (77.1) by

(77.5) $$a_{n-k}x^k + a_n = 0,$$

and a formula like (77.4) can be readily deduced.

78. Horner's Method.—Consider the polynomial

$$(78.1) \qquad f(x) = x^3 - 2x^2 - 5x + 7.$$

We have by synthetic substitution

$$f(1) = +, \quad f(2) = -, \quad f(3) = +, \quad f(-3) = -, \quad f(-2) = +.$$

Hence the equation has three real roots of the form $+1. \cdots$, $+2. \cdots$, and $-2. \cdots$, which we shall compute in the order indicated.

1	-2	-5	$+7$	1
	$+1$	-1	-6	
1	-1	-6	$+1$	
	$+1$	$+0$		
1	$+0$	-6		
	$+1$			

(78.2) $f_2 =$

1	$+1$	-6	$+1$	.1
	$+0.1$	$+0.11$	-0.589	
1	$+1.1$	-5.89	$+0.411$	
	$+0.1$	$+0.12$		
1	$+1.2$	-5.77		
	$+0.1$			

(78.3) $f_3 =$

1	$+1.3$	-5.77	$+0.411$	.07
	$+0.0\ 7$	$+0.09\ 59$	$-0.397\ 187$	
1	$+1.3\ 7$	$-5.67\ 41$	$+0.013\ 813$	
	$+0.0\ 7$	$+0.10\ 08$		
1	$+1.4\ 4$	$-5.57\ 33$		
	$+0.0\ 7$			

(78.4) $f_4 =$

1	$+1.5\ 1$	$-5.57\ 33$	$+0.013\ 813$	.002
	$+0.0\ 0\ 2$	$+0.00\ 30\ 24$	$-0.011\ 140\ 552$	
1	$+1.5\ 1\ 2$	$-5.57\ 02\ 76$	$+0.002\ 672\ 448$	
	$+0.0\ 0\ 2$	$+0.00\ 30\ 28$		
1	$+1.5\ 1\ 4$	$-5.56\ 72\ 48$		
	$+0.0\ 0\ 2$			

(78.5) $f_5 = 1 \quad +1.5\ 1\ 6 \quad -5.56\ 72\ 48 \quad +0.002\ 672\ 448$

$$x = 1.172\ 480\ 0 \ \pm\ .000\ 000\ 1$$
$$x = 1.172\ 480 \qquad \text{to six decimals}$$
$$x = 1.172\ 4 \qquad \text{to five digits}$$

The roots of (78.1) are diminished by 1 to give the polynomial (78.2), above, which has a root between 0 and 1 because (78.1) has a root between 1 and 2.   If y^2 and y^3 are so small that their sum can be neglected, (78.2) can be approximated by the linear equation

$$-6y + 1 = 0,$$

whose root to one digit is $y = .1$.   We *tentatively* assume that this is the second digit of x.

Diminishing the roots of (78.2) by .1 gives (78.3), whose linear equation is

$$-5.77z + 0.411 = 0.$$

The value of z to one significant digit is $z = .07$.   We assume tentatively $x = 1.17$ to three digits.

Diminishing the roots of (78.3) by .07 gives (78.4), whose linear equation is

$$-5.57\ 33t + 0.013\ 813 = 0,$$

so that $t = .002$, approximately.

Finally, diminishing the roots of (78.4) by .002 gives (78.5). Its linear equation has a root slightly less than .0005.   Now .0005 is easily substituted in (78.5) mentally, if we only want the result to four decimals because the first two terms do not affect the answer.   Thus we have

$$f_5(.000\ 4) = +, \qquad f_5(.000\ 5) = -.$$

Consequently the root of f is less than .000 5.   In the numerator of (77.4) we accordingly take $A = 2$, $B = .000\ 5$.   The denominator[1] obviously exceeds 5, so that we have as an upper limit to the error .000 000 1, that is, if the root of

---

[1] It is usually obvious that the integral part of $|a_{n-1}|$ is less than $|a_{n-1}|(1 - B)$, so that the denominator can be replaced by the integral part of $|a_{n-1}|$.

(78.5) is computed from the linear equation, the error is less than .000 000 1. By division we find the root of the linear equation to be .000 480 0. The value of x is obtained by increasing this root by $1 + .1 + .07 + .002$ and is as shown.

Note that the digits .1, .07, .002, which were adopted tentatively, have all been proved correct by the final evaluation of the error. The approximation that seems the one to adopt may not always be right, however. Exactly what may happen, when the tentative approximation is too large or too small, is illustrated in the computation of the next root.

Since the second root lies between 2 and 3, the roots are diminished by 2 to give (78.6). The linear equation, however, has root -3. As the root should be between 0 and 1, the higher powers of y obviously cannot be neglected. This probably means that the root is nearer 1 than 0. The relations $f(2) = -3$, $f(3) = +1$ confirm this, and indicate that the root is about $\frac{3}{4}$ of the way from 0 to 1. Hence we choose .7 as a tentative approximation (.7 is chosen rather than .8, because even if the root is exactly $\frac{3}{4}$, .7 is the value correct to one digit).

Diminishing (78.6) by .7 gives (78.7), whose linear equation has the root .2. This indicates that the approximation to the root of (78.6) is *too small* by approximately .2. The roots of (78.6) should accordingly be diminished by .9. This is most easily accomplished by diminishing the roots of (78.7) by .2. It becomes apparent, after the constant term is computed, that .2 is too large, for the next approximation would be negative. Hence the operation is immediately halted, and .2 is replaced by .1. The rest of the computation presents no peculiarities.

Accordingly we note that

(i) if the solution of a linear equation is positive and affects a digit already computed, that digit is probably too small;

(ii) if it is negative, the digit is probably too large.

	1	−2	−5	+ 7	2
		+2	+0	−10	
	1	+0	−5	−3	
		+2	+4		
	1	+2	−1		
		+2			
(78.6)	1	+4	−1	−3	.7
		+0.7	+3.29	+1.603	
	1	+4.7	+2.29	−1.397	
		+0.7	+3.78		
	1	+5.4	+6.07		
		+0.7			
(78.7)	1	+6.1	+6.07	−1.397	.2
		+0.2	+1.26	+1.466	
	1	+6.3	+7.33	+0.069	
(78.8)	1	+6.1	+6.07	−1.397	.1
		+0.1	+0.62	+0.669	
	1	+6.2	+6.69	−0.728	
		+0.1	+0.63		
	1	+6.3	+7.32		
		+0.1			
(78.9)	1	+6.4	+7.32	−0.728	.09
		+0.0 9	+0.58 41	+0.711 369	
	1	+6.4 9	+7.90 41	−0.016 631	
		+0.0 9	+0.59 22		
	1	+6.5 8	+8.49 63		
		+0.0 9			
(78.10)	1	+6.6 7	+8.49 63	−0.016 631	.001
		+0.0 0 1	+0.00 66 71	+0.008 502 971	
	1	+6.6 7 1	+8.50 29 71	−0.008 128 029	
		+0.0 0 1	+0.00 66 72		
	1	+6.6 7 2	+8.50 96 43		

$$x = 2.891\ 955\ \pm\ .000\ 001$$
$$x = 2.892\ 0 \quad \text{to four decimals}$$
$$x = 2.891\ 95 \quad \text{to six digits}$$

These, however, are only indications. The solution of the linear equation in the case of (78.6) is negative, although the approximation is known to be right. In exceptional cases of that sort, we can always determine the digit exactly by synthetic substitution, although this may be very tedious when the equation has more than one root between a pair of consecutive integers.

The negative root between -2 and -3 is found by computing the root between 2 and 3 for

$$-f(-x) = x^3 + 2x^2 - 5x - 7.$$

As a partial check, the roots are added. The sum differs from what it should be by only .000 001.

1	+2	− 5	−7	2
	+2	+ 8	+6	
1	+4	+ 3	−1	
	+2	+12		
1	+6	+15		
	+2			
1	+8	+15	−1	.06
	+0.0 6	+ 0.48 36	+0.929 016	
1	+8.0 6	+15.48 36	−0.070 984	
	+0.0 6	+ 0.48 72		
1	+8.1 2	+15.97 08		
	+0.0 6			
1	+8.1 8	+15.97 08	−0.070 984	.004
	+0.0 0 4	+ 0.03 27 36	+0.064 014 144	
1	+8.1 8 4	+16.00 35 36	−0.006 969 856	
	+0.0 0 4	+ 0.03 27 52		
1	+8.1 8 8	+16.03 62 88		

$$-x = 2.064\ 434\ 6 \pm .000\ 000\ 2$$
$$-x = 2.064\ 43 \qquad \text{to five decimals}$$
$$-x = 2.064\ 434 \qquad \text{to seven digits}$$

The gist of the foregoing procedure is as follows. By Sturm's theorem or by Theorem 73.1 the root is located between consecutive integers a and $a + 1$. The method of Sec. 65 is then applied to diminish the roots by a. The new equation has a root between 0 and 1. Its value $.b$ to one decimal place is computed by the method of Sec. 77, or that failing, by synthetic substitution and application of Theorem 73.1. The roots are again diminished, this time by $.b$. The resulting equation has a root between 0 and .1. This is continued until about four digits of the root are known. An application of Sec. 77 will then usually give about four more digits by division.

It is often required to find the value of the root "correct to so many decimal places." We shall interpret this to mean that the approximation differs from the exact value by five units or less in the first unwritten decimal place. Thus if the exact value is 2.305 46, the value correct to three decimal places is 2.305; to four, it is 2.305 5. In order to make the value unique in all cases, we agree that the value of 1.745 to two places is 1.75.

On the other hand, we shall say that 1.74 is the value of 1.745 correct to three digits. In counting digits, a zero which is preceded only by zeros is ignored.

As is true for all computations, neatness is a prerequisite to accuracy, and both of these are prerequisites to speed.

In computing the roots, it will be found convenient to space the decimals as shown in groups of one, two, three, four, $\cdot \cdot \cdot$ digits as the synthetic division advances from left to right.

EXERCISES

Compute all the real roots of the following polynomials correct to six digits. State exactly to how many digits and to how many decimals your computations actually give the root. Check the results by forming the sum or by substitution.

78.1. $x^2 - 2$.

78.2. $3x^2 + x - 1$.

78.3. $x^3 - 9$.

78.4. $x^3 - 3x^2 + 9x - 8$.

78.5. $x^3 - 5x^2 + 10x - 11$.

78.6. $x^3 - 3x^2 + 4x + 9$.

78.7. $x^3 + 3x^2 - 3x - 3$.

78.8. $x^4 + 2x^3 - 3x^2 - 4x - 2$.

78.9. $x^4 + x^3 - 7x^2 - x + 5$.

78.10. For the polynomial $x^5 + 10x - 1$ devise a special means of evaluating the error and compute the root correct to five digits.

78.11–78.14. Find the real roots in Exercises 78.3–78.6 (to the accuracy allowed by the tables) by using hyperbolic functions (Sec. 69).

CHAPTER IX

SYMMETRIC FUNCTIONS

This chapter is primarily concerned with developing properties of symmetric functions of n indeterminates, which can always be interpreted as representing the roots of an equation of the nth degree in a single indeterminate. First of all, however, we must define polynomials in more than one indeterminate. It will be convenient to develop here not only properties useful in this chapter but also others not needed until later.

79. Polynomials in Several Indeterminates.—The expression

$$ax_1^{j_1}x_2^{j_2} \cdots x_n^{j_n},$$

where the j's are non-negative integers, the x's indeterminates, and a constant, is called a *monomial* of which a is the coefficient. If $a \neq 0$, its *degree* is $j_1 + j_2 + \cdots + j_n$, and its degree in the particular indeterminate x_k is j_k.

The sum of a finite number of monomials is a *polynomial*. The sum, difference, and product of two such polynomials with coefficients from a ring R are readily seen to be polynomials with coefficients from R. Their totality therefore forms a ring (Sec. 1), which we shall denote by

$$R[x_1, x_2, \cdots, x_n].$$

If quotients of the polynomials in $\mathfrak{F}[x_1, x_2, \cdots, x_n]$, where $\mathfrak{F}$ is a *field*, are formed in all possible ways, there results a set, denoted by $\mathfrak{F}(x_1, x_2, \cdots, x_n)$, which is readily proved a field and whose members are called *rational functions* of the x's with coefficients in $\mathfrak{F}$.

It is clear that any polynomial in $R[x_1, x_2, \cdots, x_n]$ can be formally written as a polynomial in the single indeterminate x_n with coefficients in $R[x_1, x_2, \cdots, x_{n-1}]$. If $x_1, \cdots, x_{n-1}$ are replaced by constants in R, this polynomial becomes a member of $R[x_n]$.

Two monomials are called *like* if their exponents $j_1 j_2 \cdots j_n$ are the same. If all like monomials have been combined into single terms, a polynomial is said to be in *standard form*. The coefficients of the standard form are unique because of the fundamental laws of combination for our symbols (Sec. 1). They will be called the coefficients of the polynomial.

A polynomial is *identically zero* if it is equal to zero whatever values from R are assigned to its indeterminates. We shall next prove

Theorem 79.1.—*A polynomial is identically zero if and only if its coefficients are zero.*

That the polynomial is zero if its coefficients are zero is obvious, so we need only prove the other statement of the theorem. We shall prove it on the assumption that R contains infinitely many numbers, as does every ring of complex numbers except the trivial ring consisting of 0.

The statement is true for one indeterminate. For if the polynomial f is zero for all values in R, the polynomial f cannot have definite degree because of Theorem 32.3, which is true even for degree zero. Hence f is the polynomial 0, that is, all its coefficients are zero.

Now let a polynomial in n indeterminates be written as a polynomial in the single indeterminate x_n. Its coefficients $a_1, a_2, \cdots$ are polynomials in $n - 1$ indeterminates which must be zero for all values of those indeterminates. For if the $n - 1$ indeterminates are replaced by any values from R, the polynomial becomes an identically vanishing polynomial in x_n, whose coefficients must therefore be zero by the statement for a single indeterminate already proved. Hence $a_1, a_2, \cdots$ are identically vanishing polynomials in $x_1, \cdots,$ x_{n-1}. If the theorem is assumed for $n - 1$ indeterminates, the coefficients of $a_1, a_2, \cdots$, which together constitute the coefficients of f, must be zero. Hence the theorem is true for n indeterminates and the induction is complete.

Two polynomials f, g are *identically equal* if they are equal for all values of the indeterminates. This is equivalent to saying that $f - g$ is identically zero. Hence we have

THEOREM 79.2.—*Two polynomials are identically equal if and only if the coefficients of like terms are equal.*

If the degree of a polynomial in each of its indeterminates does not exceed unity, the polynomial is called *multilinear*. Thus

$$1 + x_1 + x_2 + x_1x_2 + x_3x_4x_5$$

is a multilinear polynomial.

The following result will be useful later.

THEOREM 79.3.—*If a multilinear polynomial has a non-zero coefficient (does not vanish identically), the equation obtained by placing it equal to zero can be solved for one of the indeterminates as a rational function of the others.*

Let the non-zero coefficient be in a term containing x_n. The polynomial can be written

$$ax_n + b,$$

where a, b are multilinear polynomials in $n - 1$ indeterminates. Since a has a non-zero coefficient, it is not identically zero, and we have the desired result.

80. Conjugates.—The two symbols x_1, x_2 are called *conjugate*[1] (under the symmetric group of degree n) because the

---

[1] If x_1, x_2 are the roots of $x^2 + 1 = 0$, then $a + bx_1$ and $a + bx_2$ are conjugates according to the above definition, which is therefore in

group contains a permutation (12) which carries x_1 into x_2. Likewise, x_1, x_2, $\cdots$, x_n are all conjugate. They form, moreover, a set which is closed under the operation of applying a permutation from the symmetric group of degree n. Their sum $x_1 + x_2 + \cdots + x_n$ is invariant under the group, that is, it remains unaltered when any permutation is applied to it. Thus (12) gives $x_2 + x_1 + \cdots + x_n$, which because of the commutative law of addition satisfied by the indeterminates is the same as the original $x_1 + x_2 + \cdots + x_n$.

A polynomial (or function) which is left invariant by every permutation of the symmetric group is called *symmetric*.

81. Σ-polynomials.—Any unit monomial in the indeterminates x_1, $\cdots$, x_n, that is, an expression of the form

$$x_1^{j_1} x_2^{j_2} \cdots x_n^{j_n},$$

where the j's are non-negative integers, has a finite set of conjugate monomials, which can be found by applying the permutations of the symmetric group. Consider, for the sake of preciseness, all the *distinct* monomials in this set. Its sum is invariant. For if we call the monomial M and employ the notation (13.3) for the whole symmetric group, the complete set of unit monomials conjugate to M is[1]

(81.1) $\qquad MS_1, \qquad MS_2, \qquad \cdots, \qquad MS_k,$

and the result of applying T to them is

(81.2) $\qquad MS_1T, \qquad MS_2T, \qquad \cdots, \qquad MS_kT.$

As in Sec. 13, the symbols (81.1) are the same as (81.2) except for the order in which they are written. Hence the sum of the distinct symbols on the two lines is the same.

---

harmony with the practice (Sec. 43) of calling $a + bi$ and $a - bi$ conjugate complex numbers.

[1] The object on which the permutation operates is put immediately to the left of it.

The symmetric polynomial obtained in the above manner is a Σ-*polynomial*.   Any one of its monomials is said to *generate* it.   The elementary symmetric polynomials are those generated by the monomials

$$x_1, \qquad x_1x_2, \qquad \cdots, \qquad x_1x_2 \cdots x_n.$$

A fundamental result is given in

THEOREM 81.1.—*Every symmetric polynomial with integral coefficients is a linear combination with integral coefficients of* Σ-*polynomials.*

To prove this, let the symmetric polynomial P contain the monomial aM, where a is the coefficient.   If the permutation S carries P into P', then P' contains the monomial $a(MS)$.   So also must its equal P.   Hence all the monomials conjugate to M occur in P with the *same* coefficient a.   They can therefore be grouped together to form a Σ-polynomial.   If they do not exhaust the monomials of P, the operation is repeated.

EXERCISES

81.1. Write the permutations of the symmetric group of degree 3, apply them to x_1, x_1x_2, $x_1x_2^2$ and $x_1x_2^2x_3^3$, and thus tabulate the conjugates of those monomials.

81.2. Write the permutations of the symmetric group of degree 4 and apply them to the monomials in Exercise 81.1.

82. Weight and Index.—The elementary symmetric polynomials will be denoted by $E_1, \cdots, E_n$.   The subscript on E_j will be called its *weight*, and the weight of a product of E's will be by definition the sum of the weights of its factors. Thus the weight of $E_1^2E_2E_3^3$ is 13.

If the exponents of the monomial $M = x_1^{i_1}x_2^{i_2} \cdots x_n^{i_n}$ are written in descending order of magnitude, the resulting symbol $j_1 \cdots j_n$ is called the *index* of the monomial.   Thus

$x_1^2 x_2^3 x_3 x_4^3 x_5 x_6^0$ has index 332110, which will usually be written 33211, with the zero omitted. If exponents greater than nine are involved, it becomes necessary to separate the digits in the index, say, by commas. Thus $x_1^{10} x_2^5$ has index 10,5. The elementary symmetric polynomials have indices 1, 11, 111, $\cdots$, 1 $\cdots$ 1.

A monomial M of index $j_1 \cdots j_n$ is said to be *higher*[1] than a monomial M' of index $k_1 \cdots k_n$ either if M is of higher degree than M'; or if it is of the same degree if at least one of the differences

$$(82.1) \qquad j_1 - k_1, \qquad j_2 - k_2, \qquad \cdots, \qquad j_n - k_n$$

is not zero, and if the first non-zero difference in (82.1) is positive. For convenience, if M is higher than M', we say that the index of M is greater than that of M'.

The index of a Σ-polynomial is defined as the index of any one of its monomials. Two Σ-polynomials are the same if and only if they have the same index. Hence a Σ-polynomial is completely characterized by its index (and the number of indeterminates, if the above convention of omitting zeros from the index is followed).

We define the sum of two indices as the result of adding the numbers in corresponding places. Thus $3321 + 412 = 7441$. With this understanding we have

THEOREM 82.1.—*The product of two Σ-polynomials is a sum of Σ-polynomials whose indices do not exceed the sum of the indices of the factors.*

Let the indices of the two polynomials P, Q be $j_1 \cdots$ and $k_1 \cdots$. The product PQ is obviously of degree not exceed-

---

[1] A more appropriate term would perhaps be *absolutely higher*. The term "higher" as usually employed denotes a property dependent on the order in which the indeterminates are written.

ing $j_1 + k_1$ in each of the indeterminates. Hence the first
number in the index of every term of PQ does not exceed
$j_1 + k_1$.

Any term containing only lower powers than $j_1 + k_1$ will
have index less than the sum of the indices, so that we now
confine our attention to the terms of PQ containing $x_1^{j_1+k_1}$.
We may write

$$P = x_1^{j_1}P_1 + P_2, \qquad Q = x_1^{k_1}Q_1 + Q_2,$$

where P_1, Q_1 do not involve x_1 and P_2, Q_2 are of lower degree
in x_1 than j_1, k_1, respectively.   We can see that the polynomials
P_1, Q_1 are Σ-polynomials in $x_2, \cdots, x_n$ in the following
manner.   If m_1, m_2 are monomials of P_1, then $x_1^{j_1}m_1$, $x_1^{j_1}m_2$ are
conjugate under a permutation S of the symmetric group of
degree n because P is a Σ-polynomial.   Clearly S leaves x_1
unaltered since m_1, m_2 do not contain x_1.   Hence S is a permutation of degree $n - 1$.   Conversely, every monomial in x_2,
$\cdots, x_n$ conjugate to m_1 will be contained in P_1, and the
desired point is established for P_1.   The same argument
applies to Q_1.

Now any term of PQ containing $x_1^{j_1+k_1}$ will be contained in
$x_1^{j_1+k_1}P_1Q_1$.   The indices of P_1 and Q_1 are, moreover, obtained
by omitting j_1 and k_1 from those of P and Q.   If the truth
of the theorem is admitted for $n - 1$ indeterminates, it therefore follows for n indeterminates.   In the case of one indeterminate, the index becomes the degree and the theorem is
obvious.   Hence the induction is complete.

83. The Fundamental Theorems.—The material in Sec. 82
will be useful in proving

THEOREM 83.1.—*Every Σ-polynomial which is not an
elementary symmetric polynomial can be written as a polynomial in lower Σ-polynomials, the coefficients being integers.*

Let the index of the Σ-polynomial P be $j_1 \cdots j_k$. Then $P = \Sigma x_1^{j_1} x_2^{j_2} \cdots x_k^{j_k}$. Consider the product

$$(83.1) \qquad (\Sigma x_1^{j_k} \cdots x_k^{j_k})(\Sigma x_1^{j_1 - j_k} \cdots x_{k-1}^{j_{k-1} - j_k}).$$

Each term of P occurs once and only once in the expanded form of this product. The aggregate of terms with index $j_1 \cdots j_k$ is P. By Theorem 82.1 all the other terms are lower.

Some of the terms not in P occur more than once in (83.1). By counting the number of times they occur and transposing, we get an identity of the form

$$(83.2) \qquad P = QR - \Sigma a_\lambda S_\lambda,$$

where QR is the product (83.1), where the a's are integers, and where R and the S's are Σ-polynomials which are lower than P. The theorem is accordingly proved provided Q is lower than P. This is true unless $j_1 = \cdots = j_k$.

In the exceptional case, we replace (83.1) by

$$(\Sigma x_1 \cdots x_k)^{j_1}.$$

The Σ-polynomial in parentheses is lower than P provided $j_1 > 1$. If $j_1 = 1$, P reduces to an elementary symmetric polynomial, to which the theorem does not apply. Hence the proof is complete.

Repetition of the process on the polynomials in the right member of (83.2) is halted when the only polynomials occurring are elementary symmetric polynomials.

Moreover, it is to be noted that the sum of the degrees of the polynomials appearing in any term of P is equal to the degree of P. Therefore the weight of each term of the final result is the degree of P and we have

THEOREM 83.2.—*Every Σ-polynomial of degree k is a polynomial of weight k in the elementary symmetric polynomials with integral coefficients.*

By use of Theorem 83.1 we find the important result

THEOREM 83.3.—*Every symmetric polynomial with integral coefficients is a polynomial in the elementary symmetric polynomials with integral coefficients.*

Illustrative Examples.—Consider the Σ-polynomial generated by $x_1^2 x_2$. To express it in terms of the elementary symmetric polynomials, factor from its generator the largest possible monomial with equal exponents and get $x_1 x_2 \cdot x_1$. Then write the product of the polynomials generated by these factors,

$$\Sigma x_1 x_2 \Sigma x_1.$$

This product consists of the sum of all possible products of a monomial from the first by a monomial from the second. The products are therefore of one of the two types $x_1^2 x_2$ or $x_1 x_2 x_3$ according as the monomials have one indeterminate in common or no indeterminate in common. Hence we have

$$(83.3) \qquad \Sigma x_1 x_2 \Sigma x_1 = a \Sigma x_1^2 x_2 + b \Sigma x_1 x_2 x_3,$$

where the coefficients a, b are still to be determined. The monomial $x_1^2 x_2$ can arise in only one way, namely, by taking $x_1 x_2$ from the first factor and x_1 from the second, so that $a = 1$. On the other hand, $x_1 x_2 x_3 = x_1 x_2 \cdot x_3 = x_1 x_3 \cdot x_2 = x_2 x_3 \cdot x_1$ so that every term in $\Sigma x_1 x_2 x_3$ is obtained in three ways, that is, three times; and $b = 3$. Hence, denoting by E_i the elementary symmetric polynomial of weight i, we have

$$(83.4) \qquad \Sigma x_1^2 x_2 = E_1 E_2 - 3 E_3.$$

Note that the weight of the right member equals the degree of the left. Let the reader verify that the number of terms on the right of (83.3) is the same as that on the left by counting them.

Next we compute

$$\Sigma x_1^3 x_2.$$

We must evaluate the product on the left of

$$\Sigma x_1 x_2 \Sigma x_1^2 = \Sigma x_1^3 x_2 + \Sigma x_1^2 x_2 x_3.$$

The terms are of the two types indicated because x_1^2 has to be multiplied by a monomial having the factor x_1 in common with it or by one relatively prime to it. The coefficients are both unity because $x_1^3 x_2$, $x_1^2 x_2 x_3$ can only be obtained by taking x_1^2 from the second factor.

To evaluate the two sums Σx_1^2, $\Sigma x_1^2 x_2 x_3$ write

$$\Sigma x_1 \Sigma x_1 = \Sigma x_1^2 + 2\Sigma x_1 x_2;$$
$$\Sigma x_1 x_2 x_3 \Sigma x_1 = \Sigma x_1^2 x_2 x_3 + 4\Sigma x_1 x_2 x_3 x_4,$$

the coefficient 4 arising from the circumstance that any one of the four letters in $x_1 x_2 x_3 x_4$ can be taken from the second factor and the other three are then uniquely determined and come from the first. From the above relations

$$\Sigma x_1^2 = E_1^2 - 2E_2, \qquad \Sigma x_1^2 x_2 x_3 = E_1 E_3 - 4E_4.$$

Substitution in the first gives

(83.5) $$\Sigma x_1^3 x_2 = E_1^2 E_2 - E_1 E_3 - 2E_2^2 + 4E_4.$$

To illustrate further the determination of the coefficients, consider

$$\Sigma x_1 x_2 x_3 \Sigma x_1^3 x_2 = \Sigma x_1^3 x_2^2 x_3 + 3\Sigma x_1^3 x_2 x_3 x_4 + 2\Sigma x_1^2 x_2^2 x_3 x_4 + 4\Sigma x_1^2 x_2 x_3 x_4 x_5.$$

The monomial from the first factor taken with $x_1^3 x_2$ may have $x_1 x_2$ or just x_1 or just x_2 or no factor in common with $x_1^3 x_2$. Thus arise the four types on the right. To get $x_1^3 x_2 x_3 x_4$, we must take x_1 from the first factor and x_1^2 from the second, but any one of x_2, x_3, x_4 may be taken from the second. To get $x_1^2 x_2^2 x_3 x_4$, we may take x_2 from the first and $x_1^2 x_2$ from the second or x_1 from the first and $x_1 x_2^2$ from the second; in either case the whole contribution of the first factor is uniquely determined. Finally, any one of the four x_2, x_3, x_4, x_5 may be taken from the second factor in obtaining $x_1^2 x_2 x_3 x_4 x_5$.

In the identity

$$\Sigma x_1 x_2 \Sigma x_1 x_2 x_3 = \Sigma x_1^2 x_2^2 x_3 + 3\Sigma x_1^2 x_2 x_3 x_4 + 10\Sigma x_1 x_2 x_3 x_4 x_5,$$

the coefficient 10 is the number of ways in which the two indeterminates coming from the first factor can be selected. It is the number of combinations of five things, two at a time.

EXERCISES

Evaluate the Σ-polynomials whose indices are given below.

83.1. 2.	**83.2.** 22.	**83.3.** 3.
83.4. 221.	**83.5.** 222.	**83.6.** 32.
83.7. 321.	**83.8.** 4.	**83.9.** 41.

83.10. 42.

84. Relation of Degree and Number of Indeterminates.—
The importance of the weight is as follows.   The formal process of finding P (of degree k) is independent of n, provided
$n \geqq k$.   Since the answer involves only $E_1, E_2, \cdots, E_k$, the
formula for P can be found by treating the case $n = k$.   This
formula, moreover, can also be applied when $n < k$, provided
we set in it $E_{n+1} = \cdots = E_k = 0$.   This corresponds to
multiplying the equation having $x_1, \cdots, x_n$ for roots by x^{k-n},
a process which introduces $k - n$ roots $x_{n+1}, \cdots, x_k$ equal
to zero.   The $E_1, E_2, \cdots, E_n$ are obviously left unaltered by
the process, whereas $E_{n+1}, \cdots, E_k$ are zero because each of
their terms contains at least one zero root.

THEOREM 84.1.—*To express a Σ-polynomial of degree k*
in terms of the elementary symmetric polynomials, we may
treat the associated polynomial in one indeterminate as of
degree k and in the result replace by zero every elementary
symmetric polynomial of weight greater than the original
degree.

The usefulness of this result will be apparent in the next
section.

EXERCISES

In each case below interpret the formula for the number of indeterminates x_i indicated.   Also establish the formula directly and compare
results.
84.1. (83.4) for $n = 2$.   **84.2.** (83.5), $n = 3$.
84.3. Exercise 83.2, $n = 2$.   **84.4.** Exercise 83.5, $n = 3$.
                84.5. Exercise 83.7, $n = 4$.

85. Sums of Powers of the Roots.—The Σ-polynomial of
index k is of particular importance and is denoted by s_k.
Thus s_1 is the sum of the roots, s_2 is the sum of their squares,
etc.

The s's can be computed recursively by *Newton's formulas.*
Because of Theorem 84.1, we may get the formula for s_k

from an associated polynomial of degree k, which we shall write

$$f(x) = x^k - E_1 x^{k-1} + E_2 x^{k-2} - \cdots + (-1)^{k-1} E_{k-1} x \\ + (-1)^k E_k.$$

If we form

$$f(x_1) + f(x_2) + \cdots + f(x_k) = 0,$$

we obviously get

$$(85.1) \quad s_k - E_1 s_{k-1} + E_2 s_{k-2} - \cdots + (-1)^{k-1} E_{k-1} s_1 \\ + (-1)^k k E_k = 0.$$

From these we can obtain $s_1, s_2, \cdots$ successively as polynomials in the E's. Thus

$$k = 1, \qquad\qquad s_1 - E_1 = 0,$$
$$k = 2, \qquad s_2 - E_1 s_1 + 2E_2 = s_2 - E_1^2 + 2E_2 = 0.$$

Conversely, by an induction based on (85.1) we immediately conclude that the E's are polynomials in the s's with *rational* coefficients. For example, $E_2 = \frac{1}{2}(s_1^2 - s_2)$.

THEOREM 85.1.—*Every symmetric polynomial with rational coefficients is a polynomial in the s's with rational coefficients.*

Instead of finding the s's successively, we may obtain s_k directly as a polynomial in the E's as follows. Division of the identity

$$(85.2) \quad (x - x_1)(x - x_2) \cdots (x - x_n) = x^n - E_1 x^{n-1} \\ + \cdots + (-1)^n E_n$$

by x^n gives

$$\left(1 - \frac{x_1}{x}\right)\left(1 - \frac{x_2}{x}\right) \cdots \left(1 - \frac{x_n}{x}\right) = 1 - P,$$

where P is a polynomial of degree n in $1/x$. Taking the natural logarithm of both sides and using the formula

$$\log (1 - z) = -z - \frac{z^2}{2} - \cdots - \frac{z^k}{k} - \cdots ,$$

which is established in texts on the differential calculus, give

(85.3)
$$\sum_{k=1}^{\infty} \frac{s_k x^{-k}}{k} = \sum_{j=1}^{\infty} \frac{Pi}{j}.$$

Hence s_k is k times the coefficient of x^{-k} in the expression on the right. An explicit formula for it can therefore be written by use of the multinomial theorem. This is called *Waring's formula*. For most purposes, in practice, it is simpler to use (85.3) or the underlying idea. Thus to find s_3 for the cubic

$$x^3 + px^2 + qx + r = 0,$$

we seek the coefficient of x^{-3} in

$$\sum \frac{(-1)^i (px^{-1} + qx^{-2} + rx^{-3})^i}{j}.$$

It is obtained from the terms with $j = 1, 2, 3$ and is

$$-r + pq - \tfrac{1}{3}p^3.$$

Hence $s_3 = -p^3 + 3(pq - r)$, a result which should be checked by the other method.

From (60.1) by logarithmic differentiation we find the interesting formula. (Note that a_0 need not be unity.)

(85.4) $$\frac{f'(x)}{f(x)} = \frac{1}{x - x_1} + \frac{1}{x - x_2} + \cdots + \frac{1}{x - x_n}.$$

Since we have

$$(x - x_1)^{-1} = (1 - x_1 x^{-1})^{-1} x^{-1} = x^{-1} + x_1 x^{-2} + x_1^2 x^{-3} + \cdots ,$$

the coefficient of x^{-k-1} on the right of (85.4) is s_k.   This remark furnishes a ready means of finding s_k in numerical examples.

Illustrative Example.—Find s_4 for the polynomial $x^3 + x^2 + 2x + 1$. The quotient f'/f can be calculated by a modification of the synthetic division of Sec. 31.

$$
\begin{array}{rrrr|rrrrr}
 & & & & 3 & -1 & -3 & +2 & +5 \\
\hline
1 & -1 & -2 & -1 & 3 & +2 & +2 & & \\
 & & & & & -3 & -6 & -3 & \\
 & & & & & +1 & +2 & +1 & \\
 & & & & & & +3 & +6 & +3 \\
 & & & & & & & -2 & -4 & -2
\end{array}
$$

The divisor is placed to the left, so that the division may proceed indefinitely to the right.   Similarly, the quotient is placed above.   The desired s_4 is the coefficient of x^{-5} in the product and is accordingly 5.

EXERCISES

85.1–85.5. Find formulas for s_2, s_3, s_4, s_5, s_6 in two ways.

For the following, find in each case by synthetic division the s_k required for the polynomial indicated.   Check by using the values of the roots which have been obtained previously.

85.6. Exercise 68.1, s_5.   **85.7.** Exercise 67.2, s_4.
85.8. Exercise 71.1, s_3.   **85.9.** Exercise 71.2, s_4.

Express in terms of the s's the Σ-polynomials whose indices are given below.

85.10. 111.   **85.11.** 21.
85.12. 22.   **85.13.** 211.

86. Symmetric Rational Functions.

—Suppose a rational function of $x_1, \cdots, x_n$, that is, a function of the form

$$f(x) = \frac{g}{h},$$

where g, h are polynomials without common factor, is symmetric.   If g, h become $\bar{g}$, $\bar{h}$ under application of a permutation, then

$$\frac{g}{h} = \frac{\bar{g}}{\bar{h}},$$

or

(86.1) $g\bar{h} - \bar{g}h = 0.$

If we admit that Theorem 3.4 remains true when the symbols are polynomials in several indeterminates, $\bar{g}$ must be a factor of g because it is relatively prime to h. Hence $\bar{g} = \lambda g$. Similarly, $\bar{h} = \mu h$. Substitution of these values in (86.1) gives $\lambda = \mu$.

Suppose now that the permutation is the transposition (12). Then since the square leaves g unaltered, $\lambda^2 = 1$. Consider the case $\lambda = -1$. Then

$$g(x_1, x_2, x_3, \cdots, x_n) = -g(x_2, x_1, x_3, \cdots, x_n).$$

Putting $x_1 = x_2$ gives

$$g(x_1, x_1, x_3, \cdots, x_n) = 0.$$

Hence g, written as a polynomial in x_1, is divisible by $x_1 - x_2$ because of the factor theorem. (Similarly for the other differences, but this fact is not needed.) In the same way, h is divisible by $x_1 - x_2$. As g, h are relatively prime, this is a contradiction, which shows that $\lambda \neq -1$. Hence $\lambda = 1$. Since g is invariant under every transposition, it is symmetric and we have

THEOREM 86.1.—*A symmetric rational function can be written as the quotient of two symmetric polynomials.*

EXERCISES

Express in terms of the elementary symmetric polynomials each of the following:

86.1. Σx_1^{-1}.   **86.2.** $\Sigma x_1 x_2^{-1}$.

86.3. Show how to obtain formulas for the sums of like negative powers of the roots.

CHAPTER X

CONSTRUCTIBILITY

The ancient Greeks in their study of geometry proposed several construction problems which remained unsolved for so long that they ultimately became known as the "famous problems of elementary geometry." Among them are the duplication of the cube, the trisection of an arbitrary angle and the construction of the regular polygon with an arbitrary number of sides. A discussion of these seems to require the use of algebra, which was far later in reaching its maturity than its precocious sister geometry. At last, however, algebra became sufficiently well developed to show that the three problems specifically mentioned above are impossible of solution under the restrictions laid down by the Greeks. A fourth of the famous problems, the construction of a square whose area equals that of a given circle, has been proved impossible by analysis. We shall discuss the first three in the present chapter.[1]

87. Ruler and Compass Constructions.—The instruments to be employed are the ruler (a rigid body with a straight edge) and the compass. The use of the ruler is restricted to drawing a straight line joining two points or to prolonging such a line indefinitely. The compass is to be used only to draw a circle with given center and radius. These restrictions on the instruments and the manner in which they are used are important: problems unsolvable from our standpoint may

[1] For an excellent and detailed treatment of the subject, the reader is referred to F. Klein's *Famous Problems of Elementary Geometry*, New York, 1930.

become solvable if other instruments are used or the ruler and compass are used in a different manner.

Suppose there are given as marks on the board or paper several line segments, including one which has been adopted as the unit length. We shall now show how to combine these by the four rational operations. We may regard all lengths as positive: to add a negative length, we subtract the corresponding positive length, etc. To add two lengths, AB and CD, the compass legs are adjusted with one on C and the other on D so that the distance between them is equal to CD.

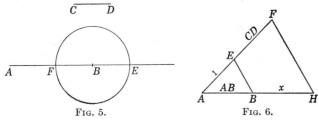

Fig. 5.   Fig. 6.

The pin is then placed at B and a circle drawn. The ruler is placed on AB, which is produced through B until it meets the circle at E. AE is then the sum $AB + CD$. To subtract the same lengths, that is, to form $AB - CD$, take the other intersection F of the same circle with AB. The difference is AF. If F falls on AB produced, the answer is negative. (See Fig. 5.)

To multiply the two lengths, draw through A a straight line making an acute angle with AB. Draw a circle with center at A and radius 1 intersecting this line at E. Construct $EF = CD$. Connect EB by the ruler. Draw FH parallel to EB. (The reader should recall for himself how this is done with ruler and compass.) Then by the geometrical theorem on proportion

$$\frac{BH}{AB} = \frac{EF}{AE} \qquad \text{or} \qquad BH = AB \cdot CD.$$

Hence BH is the desired length. Its sign can be determined from the signs of AB, CD. (See Fig. 6.)

To divide the lengths, the same figure is used with 1 and CD interchanged. From Fig. 7

$$\frac{AB}{CD} = \frac{BH}{1} = BH.$$

Let the segment AB be prolonged through B one unit. On $AB + 1$ as diameter construct a semicircle (let the reader supply the details). At B erect a perpendicular to AB. Its

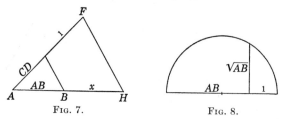

Fig. 7.   Fig. 8.

intersection with the semicircle gives the mean proportional between AB and 1, that is,[1] $\sqrt{AB}$. (See Fig. 8.)

Hence if the finite set of symbols 1, AB, CD, $\cdots$ is combined a finite number of times by the operations $+$, $-$, $\times$, $\div$, $\sqrt{\ }$, as shown above the corresponding line segments can be combined geometrically by ruler and compass to give the segment corresponding to the compound symbol.

Let us examine the converse question. Any geometric configuration consisting of lines and points may be considered as determined by the coordinates of certain points. Thus a line and a point are determined by the coordinates of three points. In order to formulate algebraically every construction with ruler and compass we must show how to find:

(i) the equation of the line joining two points;

(ii) the intersection of two lines;

[1] *Cf.* the footnote on p. 99.

(iii) the equation of a circle with given center passing through a given point or having a given radius;

(iv) the intersection of a line and a circle;

(v) the intersection of two circles.

The accomplishment of (i), (ii), (iii) is readily seen to involve only rational operations on the coordinates of the given points. (Let the reader verify this statement in detail.) As for (iv), solving the equation of the line for one of the variable coordinates in terms of the other and substituting in the equation of the circle involve only rational operations. The result is a quadratic equation in a single coordinate whose solution can be found by $+$, $-$, $\times$, $\div$, $\sqrt{\ }$ [see equation (66.2)]. Finally, case (v) can be reduced to (iv). If the equations of the two circles are

$$x^2 + y^2 + Ax + By + C = 0,$$
$$x^2 + y^2 + A'x + B'y + C' = 0,$$

subtraction gives

$$(A - A')x + (B - B')y + C - C' = 0.$$

If $A - A'$ and $B - B'$ are not both zero, this is the equation of a straight line passing through the points of intersection, that is, it is the equation of the common chord, and the intersections of the circles are its intersections with either circle. If $A - A' = B - B' = 0$, the circles are concentric.

We have therefore proved the important

THEOREM 87.1.—*A geometric figure is constructible by ruler and compass if and only if the coordinates of its points can be found by a finite number of the operations* $+$, $-$, $\times$, $\div$, $\sqrt{\ }$ *from the coordinates of the given points.*

88. Constructible Numbers.—Any rational number can be obtained from 1 by performing on it a finite number of the rational operations $+$, $-$, $\times$, $\div$. A number which can be formed from 1 by performing on it a finite number of the "ruler-and-compass" operations $+$, $-$, $\times$, $\div$, $\sqrt{\ }$ will be called a *constructible number*. We shall limit our attention to these numbers, that is, we suppose the given points have coordinates taken from the rational field.

An example of a constructible number is

$$(88.1) \qquad \frac{\sqrt{2 + \sqrt{3 - \sqrt{5}}} + \sqrt{3 + \sqrt{1 + \sqrt{5}}}}{2 + \sqrt{3}}.$$

A constructible number is said to be in *normal form*[1] if no one of its radicals can be expressed as a rational function with rational coefficients in the other radicals. Thus

$$\sqrt{2} + \sqrt{3} + \sqrt{6}$$

in normal form is $\sqrt{2} + \sqrt{3} + \sqrt{2} \cdot \sqrt{3}$. Normal form is not unique: the above number can also be written in the normal forms

$$(88.2) \qquad \sqrt{2} + \frac{\sqrt{6}}{\sqrt{2}} + \sqrt{6}, \qquad \frac{\sqrt{6}}{\sqrt{3}} + \sqrt{3} + \sqrt{6}.$$

It may be extremely hard to recognize in more complicated cases whether a constructible number is actually in normal form. For the theoretical use to which we shall put the concept, however, the knowledge that such a normal form exists is sufficient. We can convince ourselves of its existence in the following way. If one of the radicals can be replaced by a rational function of the others, we imagine this done. The process, if repeated, must ultimately terminate because it diminishes the number of radicals in the expression.

---

[1] The notion *order of a radical*, usually employed in the definition, is not necessary for our purpose.

Consider now a constructible number in normal form.[1]   The result of changing the sign of an arbitrary set of the radicals is called a *conjugate*[2] of the constructible number; and since the relation is reciprocal, the number and all its conjugates will be said to form a set of conjugates.[3] Thus $\sqrt{2} + \sqrt{3}$, $-\sqrt{2} + \sqrt{3}$, $\sqrt{2} - \sqrt{3}$, $-\sqrt{2} - \sqrt{3}$ are all conjugates. The conjugates obtained may not all be distinct: if we change the sign of the $\sqrt{3}$ in $\sqrt{2 + \sqrt{3}} + \sqrt{2 - \sqrt{3}}$, the expression is unaltered in value.

The subject next to be discussed will be made clearer by a preliminary study of the following

Illustrative Example.—Consider the constructible number

(88.3) $$x = \frac{\sqrt{1 + \sqrt{3}} + \sqrt{\sqrt{2} + \sqrt{3}}}{\sqrt{2} + \sqrt{5}}.$$

Set

$$y_1 = \sqrt{2}, \qquad y_2 = \sqrt{3}, \qquad y_3 = \sqrt{5}, \qquad y_4 = \sqrt{1 + \sqrt{3}},$$

$$y_5 = \sqrt{\sqrt{2} + \sqrt{3}}.$$

Then

$$x = \frac{y_4 + y_5}{y_1 + y_3}.$$

[1] Definition of conjugate for a number not in normal form would be difficult.   The definition given, moreover, requires that if the sign of $\sqrt{3}$ is changed in one place, it must be changed everywhere.   Otherwise the given number would be regarded as an expression in two radicals both equal to $\sqrt{3}$ and could not be regarded simultaneously as in normal form.   Thus

$$\sqrt{2 + \sqrt{3}} + \sqrt{1 + \sqrt{3}} \text{ and } \sqrt{2 - \sqrt{3}} + \sqrt{1 + \sqrt{3}}$$

are not conjugate.

[2] This use of the word "conjugate" can be connected with that in Chapter IX.   Fundamentally, the notion is the same in the two cases.

[3] A conjugate of a constructible number may be imaginary, but even in that case it is also a constructible number in the extended sense given that term in Sec. 91.

Substitute this in

$$x^3 + x + 1$$

and clear of fractions. The result is

$$(y_4 + y_5)^3 + (y_4 + y_5)(y_1 + y_3)^2 + (y_1 + y_3)^3.$$

Expanding and substituting

$$(88.4) \quad \begin{array}{ll} y_4^2 = 1 + y_2, & y_4^3 = y_4(1 + y_2), \\ y_5^2 = y_1 + y_2, & y_5^3 = y_5(y_1 + y_2), \\ y_1^2 = 2, \quad y_1^3 = 2y_1, & y_3^2 = 5, \quad y_3^3 = 5y_3 \end{array}$$

give the multilinear form

$$(88.5) \quad 2y_1y_3y_4 + 2y_1y_3y_5 + 3y_1y_4 + y_1y_5 + 4y_2y_4 + 4y_2y_5 \\ + 17y_1 + 11y_3 + 8y_4 + 10y_5.$$

Consider now the substitution of the conjugate

$$\frac{-\sqrt{1 - \sqrt{3}} + \sqrt{\sqrt{2} - \sqrt{3}}}{\sqrt{2} - \sqrt{5}}.$$

If we set

$$\bar{y}_1 = \sqrt{2}, \qquad \bar{y}_2 = -\sqrt{3}, \qquad \bar{y}_3 = -\sqrt{5}, \qquad \bar{y}_4 = -\sqrt{1 - \sqrt{3}},$$
$$\bar{y}_5 = \sqrt{\sqrt{2} - \sqrt{3}},$$

the substitution can be effected by

$$x = \frac{\bar{y}_4 + \bar{y}_5}{\bar{y}_1 + \bar{y}_3},$$

and the result can be found simply by barring all the y's in (88.5), because relations (88.4) are seen to hold if all the indeterminates are barred. Thus the coefficients are exactly the same in both cases.

It is convenient to regard the radicals appearing in a constructible number as replaced by indeterminates. The number is then a rational function with rational coefficients in certain of the indeterminates, which are in turn square roots of rational expressions in certain of the others, and so on.

The result of substituting a constructible number in normal form in an equation with rational coefficients can be written, when cleared of fractions, as a polynomial in the indeterminates. Since every indeterminate represents an expression $\sqrt{A}$, the powers higher than the first can be eliminated by means of $(\sqrt{A})^2 = A$, $(\sqrt{A})^3 = A\sqrt{A}$, etc., so that the substitution gives a multilinear polynomial in the indeterminates. If the polynomial is equal to zero, an indeterminate with non-zero coefficient can by Theorem 79.3 be expressed as a rational function of the other indeterminates. Hence *all the coefficients of the multilinear polynomial must be zero if the constructible number is a root of the equation.*

On the other hand, the polynomial obtained by substituting a *conjugate* of the constructible number arises formally from that just considered by a substitution on the indeterminates in which certain indeterminates are replaced by new indeterminates equal to conjugates of the expressions for the old. As illustrated in the above example, the coefficients will be the same as those obtained by substituting the original number because the relations like $(\sqrt{A})^2 = A$, employed in the reduction, remain true for the conjugates. Hence we have the fundamental result contained in

THEOREM 88.1.—*If a constructible number satisfies an equation with rational coefficients, all its conjugates satisfy the same equation.*

An equation with rational coefficients satisfied by the constructible number can be obtained by the process given in algebra for removing radicals. Consider the equation

$$(88.6) \qquad\qquad x - P = 0,$$

where P is a constructible number. Multiplication by constants and transposition of terms give it the form $Ay = B$, where y is a radical occurring under no other radical and A, B

are polynomials (at the start, of degree not exceeding one) in x, independent of y. Squaring this equation eliminates one radical and multiplies the degree of the equation by 2. The process is repeated until all the radicals are removed.[1] There results an equation with rational coefficients

$$F(x) = 0,$$

whose degree is 2^h, where h is an integer.

By Theorem 88.1 $F(x)$ has all the conjugates of the given constructible number for roots. On the other hand, every root of $F(x)$ is a conjugate of the original constructible number: for if we reverse the process of obtaining F, we extract square roots and any choice of signs leads ultimately to a conjugate of P. From the manner of solution it is clear that all the roots of F are simple, if all the conjugates are distinct. We shall now show that in every case the roots of F are simple and that they are the distinct conjugates in the set to which P belongs. It is sufficient to prove that the degree of F equals the number of distinct conjugates.

If (88.6) contains m distinct radicals, the maximum possible degree for F is 2^m. Let us examine the effect of the presence of two equal conjugates P, Q upon the degree of F.

Suppose changing the sign of the radicals $y_1, y_2, \cdots, y_k$ in P gives the equal Q, and suppose further that those radicals are removed in the relative order indicated by the subscripts. Let $f(x) = 0$ be the equation from which $y_1, \cdots, y_{k-1}$ have already been eliminated and from which y_k is to be eliminated by squaring. We can write

$$f = Ay_k + B,$$

where A, B are independent of $y_1, \cdots, y_k$. Since the original polynomial is unaltered by changing the signs of

---

[1] The reader will find it instructive to work Exercise 88.3 at this point.

$y_1, \cdots, y_k$, the same is true of f.   Hence we have

$$Ay_k + B = -Ay_k + B,$$

whence $A = 0$.   The elimination of y_k is automatic,[1] and the degree of the equation is not correspondingly multiplied by a factor two.   The presence of the pair of equal conjugates $P = Q$ therefore causes the degree of F to be just half what it would if P and Q were not equal.   On the other hand, the number of distinct conjugates is likewise cut in half by the equality of P and Q: if arbitrary changes of sign are introduced into P and the same changes are made in Q, equal conjugates arise.   Hence the whole set of 2^m conjugates can be written as $\frac{1}{2}2^m = 2^{m-1}$ pairs of equal conjugates.   If there are fewer than 2^{m-1} distinct conjugates, the argument can be repeated.   The degree of $F(x)$ accordingly equals the number of distinct conjugates.

$F(x)$ is determined except for a constant factor.   It is, moreover, the polynomial with rational coefficients and minimum degree having the given constructible number for one of its roots.   If $F(x)$ were equal to $G(x)H(x)$, where G, H have rational coefficients and are of lower degree than F, the constructible number would have to be a root of G or H.   Since this would contradict the minimum property of F, we see that F is irreducible.

The properties of F are summarized in

THEOREM 88.2.—*The equation obtained by removing the radicals from the linear equation defining a constructible number has for roots the distinct conjugates of that number. It is irreducible.   It is the equation of lowest degree with rational coefficients satisfied by the number.   Its degree is a power of* 2.

[1] The reader should work Exercise 88.1 at this point.

This result will be the means of proving that three of the famous problems are impossible of solution.

EXERCISES

88.1. Find $F(x)$, if $x = \sqrt{2 + \sqrt{3}} + \sqrt{2 - \sqrt{3}}$.

88.2. Is (88.3) in normal form or not?

88.3. Remove the radicals from $x = \sqrt{1 + \sqrt{2}} - \sqrt{3}$.

88.4. Verify that $\sqrt{1 - \sqrt{2}} + \sqrt{3}$ satisfies the equation found in Exercise 88.3.

88.5. Write all the conjugates of the expression in Exercise 88.3. Verify that their number is the degree of the equation found in that exercise.

88.6. Write all the conjugates of (88.3).

89. Duplication of the Cube.

—This problem is to construct a cube whose volume is double that of a cube with unit edge. The edge of the desired cube must satisfy

$$(89.1) \qquad\qquad x^3 - 2 = 0.$$

If this were reducible, it would have a linear factor with rational coefficients and hence a rational root. By Theorem 62.1 any rational root is integral and a factor of 2. By Descartes' rule there is no negative root. Neither 1 nor 2 substituted for x gives zero. Hence (89.1) is irreducible. If it had a constructible root, its degree would be a power of 2 by Theorem 88.2. Since its degree is not a power of 2, it does not have a constructible root, and the construction is impossible.

90. Trisection of the Angle.

—To show that not all angles can be trisected by ruler and compass, it suffices to prove that 30° cannot be trisected. We can construct the angle of 10° if and only if we can construct sin 10°. For, given the angle, we can construct a right triangle which contains the angle and has hypotenuse equal to unity, so that the opposite leg is the sine. Conversely, if sin 10° is given, at one end of a segment equal to it erect a perpendicular and from the other end swing an arc of radius one. The intersection gives the third vertex of a right triangle containing an angle of 10°.

From trigonometry (or by applying De Moivre's theorem) we have

$$\sin 30° = 3 \sin 10° - 4 \sin^3 10°.$$

Multiply this by 2 and substitute in it

$$2 \sin 30° = 1, \qquad 2 \sin 10° = x,$$

and obtain

(90.1) $$x^3 - 3x + 1 = 0.$$

As in the preceding section, this equation is irreducible because neither $+1$ nor -1 satisfies it. It does not have a constructible root and the construction is impossible.

EXERCISE

90.1. Prove that the angles 20°, 40°, 50°, 70°, 80° cannot be constructed by means of ruler and compass.

91. The Regular Polygon of n Sides.—From the Argand diagram (Sec. 43) it is clear that constructing the regular polygon of n sides is equivalent to solving

(91.1) $$x^n - 1 = 0.$$

A point $a + bi$ of the complex plane can be constructed by ruler and compass if and only if a and b are constructible. When they are, we shall call the number $a + bi$ constructible even if it is imaginary. Since the discussion[1] of radicals in Sec. 88 and the proof of Theorem 88.1 do not assume that the numbers under the radicals are positive, all the results are immediately applicable to imaginary constructible roots.

---

[1] As already pointed out, a real constructible number may have imaginary conjugates. *Cf.* the example in Sec. 88.

We have already seen (Sec. 57) that if n is composite, the solution of (91.1) is equivalent to the solution of a set of equations of the form

$$\frac{x^{p^e} - 1}{x^{p^{e-1}} - 1} = 0,$$

where p is prime. Since this equation is irreducible (Sec. 57), it can have a constructible root only if its degree $p^{e-1}(p - 1)$ is a power of 2,

$$p^{e-1}(p - 1) = 2^h.$$

If $e \neq 1$, p is a divisor of the left member and hence also of the right, that is, $p = 2$; and for $p = 2$, the left member is indeed a power of 2. Hence one possibility is

(91.2) $p = 2,$ e arbitrary.

If $e = 1$, we have

(91.3) $p = 2^h + 1,$ $e = 1.$

Hence the only possible factors of the number of sides of a constructible polygon are 2^h and primes of the form $2^h + 1$. Moreover, no factor $2^h + 1$ can be contained more than once in n.

In order that $p = 2^h + 1$ be prime, h must itself be a power of 2. To prove this, suppose $h = ab$, where a is a prime distinct from 2. Then

$$\frac{2^h + 1}{2^b + 1} = \frac{x^a + 1}{x + 1},$$

where $x = 2^b$. Since a is odd, the division can be carried out exactly, and p is not prime. This contradiction shows that the only prime dividing h is 2, and h is a power of 2, say 2^μ. Hence we have proved

THEOREM 91.1.—*If a regular polygon can be constructed with ruler and compass, the number of its sides has the form $2^h p_1 p_2 \cdots p_l$, where the p's are distinct primes of the form $2^{2^\mu} + 1$.*

The converse of the above theorem is true,[1] but we shall not prove it.

We close this chapter with a few remarks, some of which concern the converse of Theorem 91.1 in particular cases.

In the first place, any arc can be bisected by ruler and compass as many times as we like, that is, we can construct the polygon of $2^h p_1 p_2 \cdots p_l$ sides from that of $p_1 p_2 \cdots p_l$ sides by bisecting the arcs h times. This is the geometrical reason for the presence of the factor 2^h. Moreover, we can determine (Sec. 3) integers a, b so that $ap_1 + bp_2 = 1$, that is,

$$(91.4) \qquad \frac{b}{p_1} + \frac{a}{p_2} = \frac{1}{p_1 p_2}.$$

The arcs subtended by the sides of the polygons of p_1, p_2 sides are respectively the $1/p_1$th, $1/p_2$th part of the circle. Formula (91.4) shows that if we take b of the arcs corresponding to the polygon of p_1 sides and a of those corresponding to the polygon of p_2 sides, the sum is the arc for a polygon of $p_1 p_2$ sides. (One of the integers is negative, so that there is actually subtraction of arcs.) Similarly, a', b' can be found so that

$$\frac{b'}{p_1 p_2} + \frac{a'}{p_3} = \frac{1}{p_1 p_2 p_3}.$$

And so on. Thus the problem is reduced to the construction of polygons of p sides, where p is a prime of the form $2^{2^\mu} + 1$.

[1] L. E. Dickson, *Constructions with ruler and compasses*, in J. W. A. Young's *Monographs on Topics of Modern Mathematics*, New York, 1915, p. 376.

This is the geometric aspect of replacing (91.1) by irreducible equations.

Finally, there is the actual construction of the polygons or the solution of the corresponding equations. The cases $\mu = 0$, 1 lead to $p = 3$, 5, both of which are primes. The necessary condition is fulfilled in these cases, and constructions for these polygons are given in geometry books. Hence we know the corresponding equations $x^3 = 1$, $x^5 = 1$ can be solved by square roots, a fact which can also be verified algebraically.

The cases $\mu = 2$, 3, 4 give 17, 257, 65537, all of which are prime. The corresponding equations have all been solved. Gauss treated the case of seventeen sides, solving the equation and giving a geometrical construction for the polygon.

The number $2^{2^\mu} + 1$ increases rapidly with μ. In spite of the mounting difficulties of determining whether it is a prime, its nature has been ascertained for a few values of μ greater than 4, all of which give composite numbers. It is not known whether, for still larger untested values of μ, $2^{2^\mu} + 1$ is ever prime. For additional details see the notes by R. C. Archibald in the second edition of Klein's *Famous Problems of Elementary Geometry*.

EXERCISES

Construct with ruler and compass the regular polygons for the values of n indicated. Solve the corresponding equations $x^n = 1$.

91.1. $n = 3$.   **91.2.** 4.   **91.3.** 5.

91.4. 6.   **91.5.** 8.   **91.6.** 10.

91.7. 15.   **91.8.** 17 (cf. *Famous Problems*, pp. 24–41).

CHAPTER XI

RESULTANTS AND DISCRIMINANTS

It has been seen in Chapter VIII that (roughly speaking) every equation in a single unknown has a solution. If two such equations are proposed simultaneously, the system has in general no solution. For by the factor theorem the two equations have non-constant highest common factor if they have a common root. Given a finite number of equations in one unknown it is possible to find a single equation whose roots are precisely those common to all the proposed equations. The left member of this equation is the highest common factor of the left members of the proposed system and can therefore be determined by rational operations.

In spite of the simplicity of the theory just sketched, it is convenient to give for a pair of equations in one unknown another treatment which has the advantage of introducing a polynomial in the coefficients of the two equations, called the *resultant*, whose vanishing is a necessary and sufficient condition that two equations with non-zero initials have a root in common. The resultant also will be the basis of our treatment of systems in more than one unknown.

92. The Condition That Two Polynomials Have a Root in Common.—If

$$(92.1) \qquad \begin{aligned} f &= a_0x^m + a_1x^{m-1} + \cdots + a_m, \\ g &= b_0x^n + b_1x^{n-1} + \cdots + b_n \end{aligned}$$

have a common root, by the factor theorem they both have a factor h so that

$$(92.2) \qquad f = hf_1, \qquad g = -hg_1.$$

Let us seek to determine an h of degree $p > 0$ satisfying these relations when f, g are given.

A necessary condition is the existence of two polynomials f_1, g_1 which have degrees not exceeding $m - p$, $n - p$, respectively, and which satisfy

$$(92.3) \qquad fg_1 + f_1g = 0, \qquad f_1g_1 \neq 0.$$

This condition is also sufficient: not all the n linear factors of g can be contained in g_1, whose degree does not exceed $n - p$, so that at least p linear factors of g divide f. This argument assumes that the degree of g is actually n, that is, $b_0 \neq 0$. If $a_0 \neq 0$, a similar argument can be applied.

When polynomials f_1, g_1 of degrees not exceeding $m - p$, $n - p$ satisfy (92.3), the polynomials f and g accordingly have a factor h of degree p in common, and we may write

$$(92.4) \qquad f = h\bar{f}_1, \qquad g = -h\bar{g}_1.$$

Substitution in (92.3) gives

$$(92.5) \qquad \bar{f}_1g_1 = f_1\bar{g}_1.$$

If p is known to be the degree of the *highest* common factor, $\bar{f}_1$ and $\bar{g}_1$ are relatively prime and (92.5) implies $\bar{f}_1 = \lambda f_1$, $\bar{g}_1 = \lambda g_1$, where λ is constant. Only in this case can an arbitrary solution of (92.3) be taken as the f_1, g_1 in (92.2). Compare Exercise 93.6.

EXERCISES

By computing the highest common factor find the roots of the following systems:

92.1. $\quad x^4 - x^3 - 3x^2 + 17x - 30,$
$\qquad x^3 - 3x^2 - 10x + 24.$

92.2. $\quad x^4 - x^2 - 2x - 1,$
$\qquad 2x^3 + 3x^2 + 3x + 1.$

92.3. $2x^4 - 5x^3 + 6x^2 - 4x + 1,\ x^3 - 1.$

92.4. $3x^4 + 7x^3 - x^2 - 7x - 2,$
$2x^3 + 5x^2 - x - 6.$

92.5. $x^3 + 3x + 2, x^2 - x + 1.$

93. Sylvester's Dialytic Elimination for a Special Case.—
Consider first a cubic and a quadratic polynomial,

$$(93.1) \quad f = a_0x^3 + a_1x^2 + a_2x + a_3, \qquad g = b_0x^2 + b_1x + b_2.$$

Multiply these equations by x, 1; and by 1, x, x^2, respectively,
and display the results in the following form:

$$
\begin{aligned}
xf &= a_0x^4 + a_1x^3 + a_2x^2 + a_3x, \\
f &= \qquad\;\; a_0x^3 + a_1x^2 + a_2x + a_3, \\
(93.2) \qquad g &= \qquad\qquad\quad\;\; b_0x^2 + b_1x + b_2, \\
xg &= \qquad\quad b_0x^3 + b_1x^2 + b_2x, \\
x^2g &= b_0x^4 + b_1x^3 + b_2x^2.
\end{aligned}
$$

Regard this as a linear system in the unknowns x^4, x^3, x^2, x, 1.
Let the determinant of the system be R:

$$(93.3) \qquad R = \begin{vmatrix} a_0 & a_1 & a_2 & a_3 & 0 \\ 0 & a_0 & a_1 & a_2 & a_3 \\ 0 & 0 & b_0 & b_1 & b_2 \\ 0 & b_0 & b_1 & b_2 & 0 \\ b_0 & b_1 & b_2 & 0 & 0 \end{vmatrix}.$$

R is called the *resultant* of f, g. It is also written $R(f, g)$.

If formulas (25.2) are applied to the last unknown 1, the
result is

$$R = \begin{vmatrix} a_0 & a_1 & a_2 & a_3 & xf \\ 0 & a_0 & a_1 & a_2 & f \\ 0 & 0 & b_0 & b_1 & g \\ 0 & b_0 & b_1 & b_2 & xg \\ b_0 & b_1 & b_2 & 0 & x^2g \end{vmatrix}.$$

By expanding in terms of the last column, this equation can be
written

$$(93.4) \qquad\qquad Pf + Qg = R,$$

where P, Q are polynomials in x. Since R does not contain x, equation (93.4) gives a method of combining f, g so as to eliminate x. For this reason, R is sometimes called an *eliminant* of f and g.

It is clear from (93.4) that any factor common to f and g is a factor of R. Hence a necessary condition for f, g to have a non-constant common factor is

$$(93.5) \qquad\qquad\qquad R = 0.$$

We next examine the sufficiency of this condition. To this end write

$$(93.6) \qquad f_1 = x_4 x^2 + x_3 x + x_2, \qquad g_1 = x_0 x + x_1,$$

and seek to determine $x_0, \cdots, x_4$ so that (92.3) is satisfied. Substituting these values in (92.3) and equating coefficients to zero give

$$(93.7) \quad \begin{aligned} a_0 x_0 & + b_0 x_4 = 0, \\ a_1 x_0 + a_0 x_1 & + b_0 x_3 + b_1 x_4 = 0, \\ a_2 x_0 + a_1 x_1 + b_0 x_2 &+ b_1 x_3 + b_2 x_4 = 0, \\ a_3 x_0 + a_2 x_1 + b_1 x_2 &+ b_2 x_3 = 0, \\ a_3 x_1 + b_2 x_2 & = 0. \end{aligned}$$

The determinant of this system is R with its rows and columns interchanged, that is, the *transpose* of R. By Theorem 27.3 the system has a non-trivial solution. Hence, in the presence of $b_0 \neq 0$, (93.5) is a necessary and sufficient condition for a non-constant common factor.

Next omit the first and last equation from (93.2) and consider it as a system in x^3, x^2, x. Treat it as (93.2) was treated, calling the determinant R_1 and employing the unknown x:

$$R_1 x = \begin{vmatrix} a_0 & a_1 & f - a_3 \\ 0 & b_0 & g - b_2 \\ b_0 & b_1 & xg \end{vmatrix}.$$

This can be rewritten

$$(93.8) \qquad P_1 f + Q_1 g = R_1 x + S_1,$$

where S_1 is obtained from R_1 by replacing the elements of its last column by those in the column to the right of it in R. From (93.8) it is obvious that $R_1 x + S_1$ is divisible by any common factor of f, g. If $R_1 \neq 0$, (93.8) is linear in x and furnishes the highest common factor. Now the left member of (93.8) is

$$\begin{vmatrix} a_0 & a_1 & f \\ 0 & b_0 & g \\ b_0 & b_1 & xg \end{vmatrix}.$$

As we shall see later, R_1 is the second member of a sequence of resultants, R, R_1, $\cdots$. Hence we have seen in the case under consideration that the highest common factor is obtained by replacing the last column of the first non-vanishing resultant by f, g, xg.

Suppose $R = 0$, $b_0 \neq 0$. Then there is a common factor $x - \alpha$ and, using g_1 instead of the usual $-g_1$, we write

$$(93.9) \qquad f = (x - \alpha)f_1, \qquad g = (x - \alpha)g_1.$$

The non-trivial solution of (93.7) may not furnish the corresponding f_1, g_1 (see the discussion of equation (92.5) above and Exercise 93.6 below). This will happen, for example, if the a's and b's are real and α is imaginary. In such a case, however, the polynomials f, g have in common a factor of higher degree, which can be determined by rational operations.

Let us form the resultant of the f, g given by (93.6) and (93.9), that is,

$$f = x_4 x^3 + (x_3 - \alpha x_4)x^2 + (x_2 - \alpha x_3)x - \alpha x_2,$$
$$g = x_0 x^2 + (x_1 - \alpha x_0)x - \alpha x_1.$$

Substitution in (93.3) gives

$$\begin{vmatrix} x_4 & x_3 - \alpha x_4 & x_2 - \alpha x_3 & -\alpha x_2 & 0 \\ 0 & x_4 & x_3 - \alpha x_4 & x_2 - \alpha x_3 & -\alpha x_2 \\ 0 & 0 & x_0 & x_1 - \alpha x_0 & -\alpha x_1 \\ 0 & x_0 & x_1 - \alpha x_0 & -\alpha x_1 & 0 \\ x_0 & x_1 - \alpha x_0 & -\alpha x_1 & 0 & 0 \end{vmatrix}.$$

Multiply the first column by α and add to the second; multiply the *new* second column by α and add to the third; multiply the new third column by α and add to the fourth; multiply the new fourth column by α and add to the fifth. The result is

$$\begin{vmatrix} x_4 & x_3 & x_2 & 0 & 0 \\ 0 & x_4 & x_3 & x_2 & 0 \\ 0 & 0 & x_0 & x_1 & 0 \\ 0 & x_0 & x_1 & 0 & 0 \\ x_0 & x_1 & 0 & 0 & 0 \end{vmatrix}.$$

The value of this is, of course, zero, since $R = 0$. The important thing to note, however, is that the determinant obtained by omitting the first and last rows and the first and last columns is obtained from R_1 by elementary transformations which do not change its value. On the other hand, the above form of the determinant is seen to be the resultant of f_1, g_1. Hence we have the fundamental result

$$(93.10) \qquad R_1(f, g) = R(f_1, g_1),$$

if (93.9) holds. From this we conclude that when $R = 0$ and $b_0 \neq 0$, f, g have a quadratic factor in common if and only if $R_1 = 0$. It is also clear that

$$R_2(f, g) = R_1(f_1, g_1) = b_0.$$

Hence, with $b_0 \neq 0$, and with R interpreted as R_0, the degree of the highest common factor is the *index on the first non-*

vanishing resultant.   Thus for

$R_0 \neq 0$,	the h.c.f. is constant;
$R_0 = 0$, $R_1 \neq 0$,	the h.c.f. is linear;
$R_0 = 0$, $R_1 = 0$, $R_2 \neq 0$,	the h.c.f. is quadratic.

EXERCISES

93.1. Find the resultant of two quadratics

$$ax^2 + bx + c, \qquad a'x^2 + b'x + c'.$$

93.2. Find an expression for the linear factor which the polynomials in Exercise 93.1 have in common when $R = 0$. By substituting the corresponding root in the polynomials, verify the form of the condition $R = 0$.

93.3. Deduce from the results of this section the theorem that two quadratics have the same roots if and only if their coefficients are proportional.

93.4. Find the condition that a quadratic have equal roots by expressing that $R(f, f') = 0$.

93.5. Give a discussion like that of the present section for two cubics.

93.6. Solve system (93.7) for the polynomials $f = x^3 + x$, $g = x^2 + 1$. Why can not the f_1, g_1 obtained serve in (92.2)?

94. The General Case.—Consider now the two polynomials (92.1) and assume for convenience $m \geq n$. Multiply the first by x^{n-1}, x^{n-2}, $\cdots$, x, 1 and the second by 1, x, $\cdots$, x^{m-1} to obtain the set of equations

$$
\begin{aligned}
x^{n-1}f &= a_0 x^{m+n-1} + a_1 x^{m+n-2} + \cdots + a_m x^{n-1}, \\
x^{n-2}f &= \qquad\qquad a_0 x^{m+n-2} + \quad \cdots \quad + a_m x^{n-2}, \\
&\cdots\cdots\cdots\cdots\cdots\cdots\cdots\cdots\cdots\cdots\cdots\cdots\cdots\cdots \\
f &= \qquad\qquad\qquad\qquad a_0 x^m + \quad \cdots \quad + a_m, \\
g &= \qquad\qquad\qquad\qquad b_0 x^n + \quad \cdots \quad + b_n, \\
&\cdots\cdots\cdots\cdots\cdots\cdots\cdots\cdots\cdots\cdots\cdots\cdots\cdots\cdots \\
x^{m-2}g &= \qquad\qquad b_0 x^{m+n-2} + \quad \cdots \quad + b_n x^{m-2}, \\
x^{m-1}g &= b_0 x^{m+n-1} + b_1 x^{m+n-2} + \cdots + b_n x^{m-1}
\end{aligned}
$$

(94.1)

in the unknowns x^{m+n-1}, x^{m+n-2}, $\cdots$, x, 1.   Its determinant is called the *resultant $R(f, g)$* of the two polynomials.

The part of the resultant consisting of elements formally different from zero can be written down by the following rule:

Write the coefficients of the first polynomial on a number of rows equal to the degree of the second, starting each new row one place farther to the right.   Then write the coefficients of the second polynomial on a number of rows equal to the degree of the first, putting the last coefficient of the first row at the extreme right and starting each new row one place farther to the left.

The above process does not define the resultant when both polynomials are of degree zero or when one of them vanishes. We put $R = 1$ in the first case and leave it undefined in the second ($fg = 0$).

If formulas (25.2) are applied to the unknown 1 in system (94.1), equation (93.4) is again found.   Moreover, if the substitution

$$(94.2) \quad \begin{aligned} f_1 &= x_{m+n-1}x^{m-1} + x_{m+n-2}x^{m-2} + \cdots + x_n, \\ g_1 &= x_0 x^{n-1} + x_1 x^{n-2} + \cdots + x_{n-1} \end{aligned}$$

is made in (92.3), a linear homogeneous system in $x_0, \cdots,$ x_{m+n-1} is found.   The determinant is again the transpose of R.   This system has a non-trivial solution if and only if $R = 0$, and by the condition of Sec. 92 in the presence of $b_0 \neq 0$ (or $a_0 \neq 0$) this is a sufficient condition for the existence of a non-constant common factor.   Hence we have

THEOREM 94.1.—*Two polynomials with non-zero initials have a common factor of degree at least one if and only if their resultant is zero.*

R_j is defined recursively as the result of omitting the first and last rows and the first and last columns from R_{j-1}.   We find as the last of the R's

$$\begin{aligned} R_n &= \pm b_0^{m-n}, \quad \text{if } m > n, \\ R_{m-1} &= a_0 b_1 - a_1 b_0, \quad \text{if } m = n. \end{aligned}$$

It is convenient to define $R_m = 1$, if $m = n$.   We put $R = R_0$ and call it the zero-th resultant.

Equation (93.10) follows in the general case by the same device as in Sec. 93. By repeated use of it we prove

THEOREM 94.2.—*The degree of the highest common factor of two polynomials with non-zero initials is the index of the first non-zero resultant.*

If we omit the first p and the last p rows of (94.1), consider the system as in the unknowns $x^{m+n-p-1}, \cdots, x^p$, and apply (25.2) to the unknown x^p, we get

$$(94.3) \qquad P_p f + Q_p g = R_p x^p + S_p,$$

where S_p is a polynomial of degree $p - 1$. If p is the degree of the highest common factor as determined by Theorem 94.2, the right member of (94.3) is a polynomial of degree p and is divisible by the highest common factor. Hence it can be taken as the highest common factor.

The left member of (94.3) is a determinant described in

THEOREM 94.3.—*If the highest common factor of two polynomials f, g is of degree p, it can be obtained from the pth resultant by replacing the last column in the following way. On the last row of the coefficients of f place f, on the next to the last xf, then x^2f, and so on. On the first row of the coefficients of g place g, on the next xg, then x^2g, and so on.*

A method of obtaining the coefficient of x^{p-k} in the highest common factor is to replace the elements of the last column of R_p by the elements in the kth column to the right in R.

The quantities in (94.3) are all obtained by ring operations. Now in the solution of the system like (93.7) for the $x_0, \cdots, x_{m+n-2p+1}$ the initial x_0 may be chosen arbitrarily, and it is apparent that if we put $x_0 = -R_p b_0$, then $x_{m+n-2p+1} = R_p a_0$. Let φ denote the right member of (94.3). It differs from the h in (92.2) by a constant factor, which can be determined by comparing the initial of f with that of φf_1. Since the latter is $R_p^2 a_0$, (92.2) is equivalent to

$$(94.4) \qquad R_p^2 f = \varphi f_1, \qquad R_p^2 g = -\varphi g_1.$$

The advantage of these formulas over (92.2) is that *their coefficients can be computed from those of f, g by ring operations.* This statement is already clear in so far as it concerns φ. That it is true for f_1, g_1 is seen by solving the system like (93.7) for x_j by Cramer's rule. The result is of the form

$$R_p x_j = x_0 A_j + x_{m+n-2p+1} B_j \qquad (j = 1, \cdots, m+n-2p)$$

so that with the above choice of initials the right members are divisible by R_p and the x's are computed by ring operations.

EXERCISES

94.1–94.10. Apply the methods of the present section to determine the highest common factors of the polynomials in Exercises 92.1 to 92.5, 35.1 to 35.5. Find also the quotients f_1, g_1 and the relations like (93.4), (94.4). Check all of the results by multiplication.

94.11. Let

$$x^p - a = fg, \qquad g = b_0 x^n + \cdots + b_n, \qquad p > n > 0.$$

Prove the relations

$$R(x^p, g) = [R(x, g)]^p = b_n^p, \quad R(x^p, g) = R(a + fg, g) = R(a, g) = a^n,$$

and from the resulting equation $a^n = b_n^p$ give another proof of Theorem 59.1. [F. Mertens, Monatshefte für Mathematik und Physik, vol. 2 (1891), pp. 291–292.]

95. Discriminants.—The first column of $R(f, f')$ is divisible by a_0. Hence $a_0^{-1} R(f, f')$ is a polynomial, which is called the *discriminant* of f and denoted by $D(f)$.

The discriminants of certain polynomials computed from the above definition are given below.

$$
\begin{aligned}
&(95.1) \quad f(x) = ax + b, & D(f) &= a; \\
&(95.2) \quad f(x) = ax^2 + bx + c, & D(f) &= b^2 - 4ac; \\
&(95.3) \quad f(x) = x^3 + px + q, & D(f) &= -4p^3 - 27q^2.
\end{aligned}
$$

Thus the previous use of the term "discriminant" for the quadratic and reduced cubic is in harmony with the present definition.

Since $R(f, f')$ is a homogeneous polynomial of degree $2n - 1$ in the coefficients, $D(f)$ is a homogeneous polynomial of degree $2n - 2$. Hence $a_0^{2-2n}D(f)$ is a polynomial in the ratios $a_1/a_0, \cdots, a_n/a_0$, that is, it is a polynomial in the elementary symmetric polynomials and is therefore a symmetric polynomial in the roots of f. Regard it as a polynomial $F(x_1)$ in one of the roots x_1. Since this polynomial vanishes for $x_1 = x_2$, it must be divisible by $(x_1 - x_2)$. Similarly, for all the other differences between two roots. Hence we have

$$(95.4) \quad a_0^{2-2n}D(f) = A(x_1 - x_2)^{e_{12}}(x_1 - x_3)^{e_{13}} \cdots$$
$$(x_{n-1} - x_n)^{e_{n-1,n}},$$

where A is not divisible by any of the differences. Now A must be a constant; for if it were not, by assigning, say, $x_2, \cdots, x_n$ distinct values it could be written as a polynomial $A(x_1)$ of positive degree in one indeterminate. The values $x_2, \cdots, x_n$ could be chosen so that $A(x_1)$ was not divisible by any of the differences $x_1 - x_2, \cdots, x_1 - x_n$. By the fundamental theorem of algebra A would have at least one root, which could not be $x_2, \cdots,$ or x_n. Hence the discriminant would vanish when f had no multiple root, that is, when f and f' did not have a common factor. This absurdity proves that A is constant.

From symmetry it follows that all the exponents in (95.4) are equal. Let their common value be e. The degree of the right member in x_1 is $(n - 1)e$. That of the left member is $2(n - 1)$ because each elementary symmetric polynomial is of degree one in x_1. Hence $e = 2$, and

$$(95.5) \qquad a_0^{2-2n}D(f) = A\prod_{j<k}(x_j - x_k)^2,$$

where Π means multiply together all terms of the given type just as Σ means sum.

To evaluate A we proceed indirectly. From

$$f(x) = a_0(x - x_1)(x - x_2) \cdots (x - x_n)$$

we deduce by differentiation and substitution

$$f'(x_1) = a_0(x_1 - x_2) \cdots (x_1 - x_n),$$
$$f'(x_2) = a_0(x_2 - x_1) \cdots (x_2 - x_n),$$
$$\cdots \quad \cdots \quad \cdots \quad \cdots$$
$$f'(x_n) = a_0(x_n - x_1) \cdots (x_n - x_{n-1}).$$

There is one and only one of these equations which contains a given difference $x_j - x_k$. Multiplying the equations together and combining the $n(n - 1)$ differences in pairs of negatives $(x_j - x_k)(x_k - x_j)$ give, therefore,

$$f'(x_1) \cdots f'(x_n) = (-1)^{\frac{1}{2}n(n-1)} a_0^n \prod_{j<k} (x_j - x_k)^2.$$

On the left side of this equation, the coefficient of

$$x_1^{n-1} \cdots x_n^{n-1}$$

is obviously $n^n c_0^n$. Hence its coefficient on the right of (95.5) is

(95.6) $(-1)^{\frac{1}{2}n(n-1)} n^n A.$

Now consider in the expansion of determinant D the term containing the elements with row indices $1, 2, \cdots, 2n - 1$ and corresponding column indices

(95.7) $n + 1, n + 2, \cdots, 2n - 1, n, n - 1, \cdots, 1.$

The sign of this term is determined by the number of transpositions necessary to bring the indices (95.7) into natural order. Carrying 1 to the first position requires $2n - 2$ transpositions, and carrying n to the nth requires $n - 1$. Hence the total number is the sum

$$2n - 2 + 2n - 3 + \cdots + n - 1 = \tfrac{3}{2}n(n - 1)$$
$$\equiv \tfrac{1}{2}n(n - 1) \quad (\text{mod } 2).$$

The product of the elements in this term is

$$n^n a_0^{n-1} a_n^{n-1} = n^n a_0^{2n-2} x_1^{n-1} \cdots x_n^{n-1},$$

since from the elementary symmetric polynomials

$$a_n = (-1)^n a_0 x_1 \cdots x_n,$$

and since $n(n - 1)$ is always even. Hence the coefficient of $x_1^{n-1} \cdots x_n^{n-1}$ on the left of (95.5) is

$$(-1)^{\frac{1}{2}n(n-1)} n^n.$$

Comparison with (95.6) gives $A = 1$. Finally, we have

$$(95.8) \qquad a_0^{2-2n} D(f) = \prod_{j<k} (x_j - x_k)^2.$$

The case $a_0 = 1$ is particularly important. When we speak of the *discriminant of n indeterminates* $x_1, \cdots, x_n$, we shall mean D computed for an equation with $a_0 = 1$ and the x's for roots. Thus we have

THEOREM 95.1.—*The discriminant of n indeterminates is the product of the squares of their differences.*

EXERCISES

95.1. Using (95.8), discuss the relation of the sign of the discriminant to the nature of the roots of the quadratic and of the reduced cubic.

95.2. Find the relation between the discriminant D_4 of the quartic (71.2) and that, say D_3, of the resolvent cubic obtained by Ferrari's method in Exercise 71.6.

95.3. Find the discriminant of the nth roots of unity. Check the answer for $n = 3$ and $n = 4$.

95.4. Find the discriminant of the general cubic (67.1).

96. Alternating Polynomials.—A polynomial P in the indeterminates $x_1, \cdots, x_n$ is called *alternating* if every transposition of the symmetric group of degree n converts it into $-P$. We shall now prove

THEOREM 96.1.—*Every alternating polynomial can be written $P = D^{\frac{1}{2}}Q$, where D is the discriminant of the indeterminates and Q is a polynomial in their elementary symmetric polynomials.*

First let us prove that *the polynomial P is divisible by each difference $x_i - x_j$.* Let P be written as a polynomial in x_1. Since $P(x_1, x_2) = -P(x_2, x_1)$, we have $P(x_1, x_1) = -P(x_1, x_1)$ or $P(x_1, x_1) = 0$. By the factor theorem $P(x_1, x_2)$ is divisible by $(x_1 - x_2)$.

Hence $PD^{-\frac{1}{2}}$ is equal to a polynomial in the x's. It is invariant under every transposition because both numerator and denominator simply change sign. It is therefore a symmetric polynomial, and the result follows as stated.

CHAPTER XII

SIMULTANEOUS SYSTEMS

97. Inequations.—In order to treat systems in several unknowns adequately, it is necessary to consider inequations as well as equations. An inequation is of the form $f \neq 0$ (read "f is not zero"), where f is a polynomial. A root of the inequation is a number a such that $f(a) \neq 0$. Clearly for one unknown we have

THEOREM 97.1.—*An inequation of positive degree has for roots all complex numbers except the roots of the corresponding equation.*

Thus the quadratic inequation $x^2 - 3x + 2 \neq 0$ has for roots all complex numbers except 1 and 2.

98. Algebraic Systems.—By the term *algebraic system* we shall mean a finite set of equations and inequations of which it is proposed to find the common roots. The left members of the system will be called its *polynomials;* they will also be called its equations and inequations, that is, "the equation f" will mean $f = 0$. Let the unknowns $x_1, x_2, \cdots, x_r$ of such a system be considered in a definite order.

Let f, g be two equations of a system S. Let m, n be the maximum exponent which the last unknown has in f, g, and suppose $m \geqq n$. Let f, g be written as polynomials in the last unknown x_r. The coefficients are then polynomials in the other unknowns $x_1, \cdots, x_{r-1}$.

We now consider two systems: S augmented by the initials a_0, b_0 of f, g as *inequations;* and S augmented by the product

$a_0 b_0$ as *equation*. Every solution of S will be found in one and only one of these augmented systems.

Next form the resultants of f, g, and suppose that

$$R = R_1 = \cdots = R_{p-1} = 0, \qquad R_p \neq 0,$$

in the sense that R, R_1, $\cdots$, R_{p-1} obviously vanish for every solution of S, and R_p at least is not obviously zero. Each of the systems formed above is then replaced by two others: one in which R_p is inequation and the other in which R_p is equation.

Consider the system with $a_0 b_0 R_p \neq 0$. From (94.4) it follows that f, g can be *replaced by the single equation* φ. Let this be done, and repeat on another pair of equations involving x_r. The process is continued until there is at most one equation involving x_r. The polynomials not involving x_r may have increased in number.

If f is equation and g inequation, they can be replaced by the equation f_1 from (94.4).

If there are only inequations involving x_r, they can be multiplied together to give a single inequation.

The process is repeated for each of the unknowns x_{r-1}, $\cdots$, x_1 in turn. In this way we replace the original system by a number of systems, each of which contains at most a single polynomial involving x_r; at most one involving x_{r-1} but not x_r; at most one involving x_{r-2} and not x_r or x_{r-1}; and so on, possibly, to a single polynomial involving only the first unknown x_1.

If a polynomial involves x_j but no unknown of higher index, it is said to have *ordinal* j. By a change in notation, if necessary, the polynomials of one of the systems replacing S can be written

$$(98.1) \qquad F_{s+1}, \qquad \cdots, \qquad F_{r-1}, \qquad F_r,$$

with F_j of ordinal j. The unknowns x_1, $\cdots$, x_s are called *parametric*. If they are given any complex values, the polynomial F_{s+1} becomes a polynomial in the *single* indeterminate x_{s+1}. Its initial has been adjoined to the system as inequation and therefore does not vanish. The existence of its roots is stated by the fundamental theorem of algebra. If any one of them is substituted in F_{s+2}, that polynomial becomes a polynomial in the single unknown x_{s+2} with non-vanishing initial, and so on. We may thus construct a solution of S by proceeding from F_{s+1} to F_r. The solution can be approximated by Horner's method.

If F_{s+1} is of degree d in x_{s+1}, the other F's in (98.1) can be made of degree less than d in x_{s+1}. For if the degree of one of them, say F, is $e > d$, we may write $x_{s+1}^e = x_{s+1}^{e-d}x_{s+1}^d$ and substitute for x_{s+1}^d the expression of degree less than d furnished by F_{s+1}. Hence x_{s+1}^e is replaced by an expression of lower degree in x_{s+1}. The process can be continued until F is of lower than degree d. The only divisions required in the process are by non-vanishing initials, and the results can finally be made integral by clearing of fractions.

The foregoing indications should enable the reader to apply the theory to examples in which the numerical work does not become too involved. For a more nearly complete discussion of the theory, Chapter VI of the author's *Differential Systems*[1] can be consulted.

Let us now illustrate the method by examples. It will often be clear that certain steps outlined for the general case can be abbreviated or omitted entirely. Thus in Exercise 98.2 below the two initials are x^2 and x, if y is chosen to be eliminated first. Mental substitution of $x = 0$ in the system gives an inconsistent system, so that we may assume $x \neq 0$. Often, replacing an equation by the difference between it and another will simplify matters, although this is equivalent to performing an elementary transformation on the resultant.

[1] New York, 1937.

A judicious choice of order for the indeterminates will some-times make the computations easier.

Consider the system S

$$f = x^2 + y^2 - 5, \qquad g = xy - 2,$$

whose roots are to be found. Adopt the order x, y for the unknowns. Then

$$R(f, g) = \begin{vmatrix} 1 & 0 & x^2 - 5 \\ 0 & x & -2 \\ x & -2 & 0 \end{vmatrix}, \qquad R_1 = x.$$

It is of course necessary that $R = 0$ if f, g have a common root. The adjunction of $a_0 = 0$ would give $1 = 0$, and the adjunction of $b_0 = x = 0$ or $R_1 = x = 0$ would give $-2 = 0$, because of $g = 0$. Hence their adjunction gives systems satisfied by no roots of S, which is accordingly equivalent to

$$f = x^2 + y^2 - 5 = 0, \qquad g = xy - 2 = 0,$$
$$R = -x^4 + 5x^2 - 4 = 0, \qquad R_1 = b_0 = x \neq 0.$$

f and g can be replaced by g, because it is the common linear factor which f, g have for any x making $R = 0$. By inspection, we see that the common factor of R and R_1 is 1, so that $R = 0$ implies $R_1 \neq 0$. Consequently, S reduced to form (98.1) is

(98.2) $\qquad x^4 - 5x^2 + 4 = 0, \qquad xy - 2 = 0.$

The solutions of F_1, it happens, can be obtained by the quadratic formula and are 1, -1, 2, -2. If these values are substituted in the second equation F_2, the corresponding values of y are found to be 2, -2, 1, -1. The solution is therefore $(\pm 1, \pm 2)$, $(\pm 2, \pm 1)$, where like signs are to be read together. The important thing to note in (98.2) is that F_1 involves only x and that F_2 becomes a polynomial in y *with non-zero initial* for any value of x satisfying F_1. In this example, there are no parametric unknowns.

Next consider

$$x^4 + x^2 y^2 + y^4 - 21, \qquad x^2 - xy + y^2 - 3.$$

Write these as polynomials in y and form the resultant:

$$R = \begin{vmatrix} 1 & 0 & x^2 & 0 & x^4 - 21 & 0 \\ 0 & 1 & 0 & x^2 & 0 & x^4 - 21 \\ 0 & 0 & 0 & 1 & -x & x^2 - 3 \\ 0 & 0 & 1 & -x & x^2 - 3 & 0 \\ 0 & 1 & -x & x^2 - 3 & 0 & 0 \\ 1 & -x & x^2 - 3 & 0 & 0 & 0 \end{vmatrix}.$$

This equated to zero gives

$$36(x^4 - 5x^2 + 4) = 0,$$

whose roots are ± 1, ± 2.

For $x = 1$, the above determinant form of R becomes

$$\begin{vmatrix} 1 & 0 & 1 & 0 & -20 & 0 \\ 0 & 1 & 0 & 1 & 0 & -20 \\ 0 & 0 & 0 & 1 & -1 & -2 \\ 0 & 0 & 1 & -1 & -2 & 0 \\ 0 & 1 & -1 & -2 & 0 & 0 \\ 1 & -1 & -2 & 0 & 0 & 0 \end{vmatrix}.$$

We readily find $R_1 = 6$. For this value of x there is just one value of y because the common factor of the two polynomials is linear. Moreover, the common factor is $R_1 y + S_1$, where S_1 is formed from R_1 by replacing its last column by the numbers immediately to their right in R. We find

$$S_1 = \begin{vmatrix} 1 & 0 & 1 & -20 \\ 0 & 0 & 1 & -2 \\ 0 & 1 & -1 & 0 \\ 1 & -1 & -2 & 0 \end{vmatrix} = -12.$$

Hence the common factor is $6y - 12$ and the solution is $(1, 2)$.

The other roots are found to be $(-1, -2)$, $(2, 1)$, $(-2, -1)$.

If form (98.1) is desired, the linear factor can be obtained from R in the form $R_1 y + S_1$, where R_1 and S_1 are polynomials in x.

EXERCISES

Reduce the following systems of equations to systems of the form (98.1) and solve the resulting equations whenever feasible.

98.1. $xy + 2x^2 - 1$, $x^2 y + 2x - 3y - 4$.

98.2. $x^2 y + 2x - 3y - 5$, $xy^2 - x + y - 1$.

98.3. $x^2 + y^2 + 4x - 2y - 20$, $9x^2 + 16y^2 + 36x - 32y - 236$.

98.4. $x^2 + y^2 - 4x + 2y$, $x^2 - xy + y^2 - 5x + 4y + 4$.

98.5. $xy + x^2 - 1$, $xy - y^2 - 2$.

98.6. $yz + y + z + 1$, $zx + z + x - 3$, $xy + x + y + 1$.

98.7. $x^2 + yz + 1$, $y^2 - zx + 1$, $z^2 + xy - 3$.

98.8. $2x^2 - yz - zx - 4xy$, $2x^2 - 2yz - zx - 5xy$.

98.9. $x^2 + xy$, $xy + y^2 + x + y$.

$\quad\quad y^2 + z^2 + 2yz - 2zx - 2xy$,

98.10. $2x^2 - z^2 - 3yz + zx - 3xy$,

$\quad\quad z^2 + yz - 2zx - 2xy$.

99. Location and Computation of Imaginary Roots.—To find a complex root of

$$(99.1) \qquad f(z) = z^3 + 3z^2 + 9z + 6 = 0,$$

set $z = x + yi$ and equate real and imaginary parts to zero:

$$(99.2) \qquad x^3 - 3xy^2 + 3x^2 - 3y^2 + 9x + 6 = 0,$$
$$(99.3) \qquad y(-y^2 + 3x^2 + 6x + 9) = 0.$$

If $y = 0$, the root is real and (99.2) reduces to $f(x) = 0$, as it should. Being interested in the imaginary case, we ignore the factor y and write (99.3) as

$$(99.4) \qquad y^2 = 3(x^2 + 2x + 3)$$

By using this relation to eliminate y^2 from (99.2) we get

$$(99.5) \qquad 8x^3 + 24x^2 + 36x + 21 = 0.$$

Since the right member of (99.4) is positive (*cf.* Exercise 66.2) for all real x, the negative root of (99.5), whose existence is stated by Theorem 73.3, gives two real values of y.   These values differ only in sign, so that the two roots z are conjugate, as Theorem 63.1 says they must be.   It is readily verified that the other two roots of (99.5) are imaginary.

In the general case, a simple means of elimination like (99.4) is not at our disposal, so that we must fall back on the resultant.

Let us now illustrate the method for coefficients some of which are imaginary.   Consider the equation

$$(99.6) \qquad f(z) = z^3 - z - i = 0.$$

Substituting $z = x + yi$ and equating real and imaginary to zero give

$$x(x^2 - 3y^2 - 1) = 0, \qquad -3x^2y + y^3 + y + 1 = 0.$$

If $x = 0$, the second of these reduces to $y^3 + y + 1 = 0$, which has one real root (negative).   Hence (99.6) has one pure imaginary root, which can be found by computing the real root of $y^3 + y + 1 = 0$.

The other roots of (99.6) satisfy

$$(99.7) \qquad y^3 + (1 - 3x^2)y + 1 = 0,$$
$$(99.8) \qquad 3y^2 + 1 - x^2 = 0.$$

The resultant is

$$(99.9) \qquad \begin{vmatrix} 1 & 0 & 1 - 3x^2 & 1 & 0 \\ 0 & 1 & 0 & 1 - 3x^2 & 1 \\ 0 & 0 & 3 & 0 & 1 - x^2 \\ 0 & 3 & 0 & 1 - x^2 & 0 \\ 3 & 0 & 1 - x^2 & 0 & 0 \end{vmatrix}.$$

The eliminant is accordingly

$$(99.10) \qquad 64x^6 - 96x^4 + 36x^2 - 31 = 0.$$

Regard this as a cubic in $4x^2$ and find the corresponding reduced cubic. The discriminant of the result is negative. Hence the cubic (99.10) has only one real root. It is the root predicted by Theorem 73.3 and is positive. Hence there are two real values $\pm\beta$ for x.

From (99.9) it follows that

$$R_1 = 6(4x^2 - 1).$$

By synthetic substitution (99.10) is seen not to have $x^2 = \frac{1}{4}$ for a root. Hence $R_1 \neq 0$ and the highest common factor of (99.7), (99.8) is linear. It is readily found from (99.9) to be

$$6(4x^2 - 1)y - 9.$$

Hence

(99.11) $$y = \frac{3}{2(4x^2 - 1)}.$$

The method of this section is perfectly general. Cubics were chosen to illustrate it because of the relative simplicity of the computations. The cubics, of course, can also be solved by the method of Sec. 67, but there is no method corresponding to that of Sec. 67 for polynomials of degree higher than four.

EXERCISES

99.1. Find relation (99.10) directly by writing (99.7) as

$$y \cdot 3y^2 + 3(1 - 3x^2)y + 3 = 0$$

and using (99.8) to eliminate y^2 from the first term.

99.2. The roots of (99.6) have the form αi, $\beta + \gamma i$, $-\beta + \gamma i$. By writing $z = i\zeta$, show how to predict this result.

Find the roots of the following polynomials by the method of Sec. 99.

99.3. $z^3 - 1.$ **99.4.** $2z^3 + 5z^2 + 5z + 3.$

99.5. $2z^3 - 9z^2 + 30z - 13.$ **99.6.** $z^3 - iz^2 - 2i.$

99.7. $z^3 - (3i + 2)z^2 + (4i - 4)z + 2i + 4.$

MISCELLANEOUS EXERCISES

The numbers of the following exercises indicate the section to which they are especially related. They are assembled here for convenience. Some of them are more difficult than those in the text proper, and some involve a considerable extension of the theory. It is hoped that the student, in seeking help to solve them, may get an introduction to the mathematical periodicals. He will find R. Garver's *A Reading list in the elementary theory of equations*, American Mathematical Monthly, vol. 40 (1933), pp. 77–84, a useful guide to helpful information and to further problems. Specific references are made to some of the literature not mentioned in Garver's list.

1.5. A number of a ring is called a unit if it has a reciprocal in the ring. The totality of units is closed under multiplication and division.

1.6. Find the units of the ring of Gaussian integers $a + bi$, where a, b range over the ring of integers.

1.7. The numbers $a + b\sqrt{5}i$ form a ring if a, b range over the integers.

1.8. If p, q, r are fixed rational numbers, if α is a fixed root of the irreducible equation $\alpha^3 + p\alpha^2 + q\alpha + r = 0$ and if a, b, c range over the rational field, the totality of numbers $a\alpha^2 + b\alpha + c$ forms a field.

2.1. A number p of a ring is prime if it is not a unit and if its only divisors are the numbers e and pe, where e ranges over the units. Is $1 + \sqrt{5}i$ prime in the ring of Exercise 1.7?

2.2. If $n = a + b$, where a, b are positive integers, then $n!$ is divisible by $a!b!$.

2.3. If p is prime and q is an integer satisfying $0 < q < p$, then $p!$ is divisible by $q!p$.

3.7. The norm of the Gaussian integer $r = a + bi$ (Exercise 1.6) is defined as $N(r) = a^2 + b^2$. Prove that $N(r)$ is a non-negative integer, that $N(r) = 0$ if, and only if, $r = 0$, and that $N(r_1r_2) = N(r_1) \cdot N(r_2)$.

3.8. If r_1 and $r_2 \neq 0$ are Gaussian integers, define r_3 by $r_1 = q_1r_2 + r_3$, where q_1 is found from the quotient $r_1/r_2 = a + bi$ by replacing a, b by integers in the following way: a is replaced by the integer n where

$$n - \tfrac{1}{2} < a \leqq n + \tfrac{1}{2},$$

191

and b is treated similarly. Thus if $r_1 = 1 + i$ and $r_2 = 2 - i$, then $r_3 = -i$. Prove that $N(r_3) < N(r_2)$, and so establish a division algorithm for the ring. (van der Waerden.)

3.9. Solve equation (3.8) by means of continued fractions.

3.10. Find a necessary and sufficient condition that a system composed of two equations like (3.8) have a solution in integers.

4.4. Is factorization always unique in the ring of Exercise 1.7?

10.8. If S, T are permutations, give a simple rule for forming $T^{-1}ST$.

11.1. Every even permutation can be written as a product of cycles of period three.

11.2. Every even permutation of degree n can be written in terms of (123), (124), $\cdots$, $(12n)$.

A square matrix or a determinant with elements a_{jk} is called: *symmetric*, if $a_{jk} = a_{kj}$; *skew symmetric*, if $a_{jk} = -a_{kj}$; and *Hermitian*, if $a_{jk} = \bar{a}_{kj}$, where the bar denotes the conjugate complex number.

24.8. Every skew symmetric determinant of odd order is zero.

24.9. Every skew symmetric determinant of even order is the square of a polynomial in its elements.

24.10. The rank of every skew symmetric matrix is even.

24.11. Every symmetric or skew symmetric matrix contains a non-zero determinant (*principal determinant*) whose order is the rank and whose main diagonal lies along the main diagonal of the matrix.

24.12. The value of every Hermitian determinant is real.

24.13. The roots of the equation (*characteristic equation*) obtained by equating to zero the determinant with elements $a_{jk} - \delta_k^j x$ are all real if $a_{jk} = a_{kj} = \bar{a}_{kj}$.

24.14. Let D be a determinant with matrix M. Two determinants d, d' of M are called *complementary minors* of D if each consists of the elements omitted from M in obtaining the other. Prove that $D = \Sigma(-1)^s dd'$, where d is allowed to range over all determinants of order r, formed from a given set of r rows in D, and s is the sum of the indices of the rows and columns composing d. (Laplace's development.)

24.15. A matrix extending indefinitely to the right and indefinitely downward is called infinite. If D_n is the determinant formed from its first n rows and first n columns and if $\lim D_n$ exists, the limit is called the determinant of the matrix. Prove that such an infinite determinant is invariant under elementary transformations. (Kowalewski, *Determinantentheorie*, Chapter 17.)

24.16. Evaluate the infinite determinant with elements

$$a_k^j = \delta_k^j + (jk)^{-2}.$$

24.17. If D is a determinant of order n with real elements whose absolute values do not exceed M, then $|D| \le n^{\frac{1}{2}n} M^n$.

24.18. Let D be a symmetric determinant of order $n > 4$ with elements a_{ij}. If $a_{11} = \cdots = a_{nn} = 1$, if $0 \le a_{ij} < 1$ for $i \ne j$, and if every principal (see Exercise 24.11) minor of order 3 vanishes, then $D = 0$. (L. M. Blumenthal, Duke Mathematical Journal, vol. 2 (1936), p. 398.)

24.19. If none of the elements of a determinant are positive except those on the main diagonal and if the sum of the elements on each row is positive, the determinant is positive and the algebraic complements of all its elements are non-negative.

28.19. Prove that the system (28.5), in which the coefficients are integers, has a solution in integers if and only if the highest common factor of all the determinants of order equal to the rank is the same for both the original and the augmented matrix.

28.20. Discuss the solution of systems (28.1) when both coefficients and unknowns are restricted to the ring of integers. (O. Veblen and P. Franklin, Annals of Mathematics, vol. 23 (1921), pp. 1–15.)

28.21. Discuss the solution of linear systems (27.1) and (28.1) when the sign $=$ is replaced by $\ge$ or by $>$. (R. W. Stokes, Transactions of the American Mathematical Society, vol. 33 (1931), p. 782.)

28.22. If the v^k on p. 50 represent polynomials in a single indeterminate x, the definition of linear dependence still applies. Show that polynomials $v_1, \cdots, v_r$ are linearly dependent if and only if the (Wronskian) determinant in their derivatives

$$\begin{vmatrix} v_1 & v_2 & \cdots & v_r \\ v_1' & v_2' & \cdots & v_r' \\ \cdots & \cdots & \cdots & \cdots \\ v_1^{(r-1)} & v_2^{(r-1)} & \cdots & v_r^{(r-1)} \end{vmatrix}$$

is identically zero.

28.23. Solve the infinite linear system

$$a_{ij}x_j = b_i \qquad (i, j = 1, 2, \cdots, \infty),$$

where $a_{ij} = (2j - 1)^{2i-2}$ and $b_1 = 1$, $b_i = 0$ $(i > 1)$. (F. Riesz, *Les Systèmes d'Equations Linéaires à une Infinité d'Inconnues*, Paris, 1913, p. 3; M. Bôcher and L. Brand, Annals of Mathematics, (2), vol. 13 (1912), p. 167.)

39.1. Determine by trial a quadratic polynomial with integral coefficients dividing $x^4 + 4x^3 - 4x^2 - 17x + 10$. (A. F. Frumveller, American Mathematical Monthly, vol. 24 (1917), p. 208.)

40.3. If the terms of degree not exceeding $n - k$ in f form a polynomial satisfying the hypothesis of Eisenstein's theorem, then f has an irreducible factor of degree $\geqq n - k$. (For $k = 0$, this is Eisenstein's theorem.)

40.4. Prove that the determinant of order n with indeterminates for elements is an irreducible polynomial in the rational field.

42.6. A polynomial of degree at most n can be found with graph passing through $n + 1$ points whose x's are arbitrary distinct real numbers and whose y's are arbitrary real numbers.

42.7. Find formulas for the coefficients in the preceding exercise.

43.8. If a convex polygon in the Argand diagram encloses the roots of $f(x)$, it also encloses those of the derivative $f''(x)$. Examine the case of roots on the boundary of the polygon.

43.9. If the roots of f are all real, those of f' are also real.

69.4. Give a solution of the cubic in terms of circular trigonometric functions of a real angle in the case of negative discriminant.

73.11. All the roots of the polynomial $x^n + a_1 x^{n-1} + \cdots + a_n$ lie within or on the circle whose center is the origin and whose radius R satisfies the inequality

$$\alpha \leqq R \leqq \alpha(\sqrt[n]{2} - 1)^{-1},$$

where α is the greatest term of the sequence

$$p_1|a_1|, \qquad p_2|a_2|^{\frac{1}{2}}, \qquad \cdots, \qquad p_n|a_n|^{\frac{1}{n}}$$

and p_k is the reciprocal of the number of combinations of n things k at a time. (G. D. Birkhoff, Bulletin of the American Mathematical Society, vol. 21 (1915), p. 494. For additional information about upper bounds to $|x|$ see E. B. Van Vleck, Bulletin of the American Mathematical Society, vol. 35 (1929), p. 643.)

75.16. If $f(x)$ is a polynomial of degree n with real coefficients, the number of its roots $\alpha + \beta i$ with $\alpha \leqq \alpha_0$ does not exceed the number of variations of sign in the sequence

$$\sum_{k=0}^{l} (-1)^k \binom{n}{k} f(\alpha_0 + kh) \qquad (l = 0, 1, \cdots, n),$$

where $\binom{n}{k}$ is the binomial coefficient and h is a positive number. (I. J. Schoenberg, Duke Mathematical Journal, vol. 2 (1936), p. 89.)

76.11. If $f = (x^2 - 1)^n$, then $f^{(n)}$ has n real roots.

78.15. Devise an abbreviated multiplication and division for decimal numbers so as to eliminate useless operations and yet give the result correct to a specified number of decimals. (E. Cahen and C. Michel, *Calcul Numérique*, Paris, 1931, p. 15.)

78.16. If b is small, an approximation to $f(a + b)$ is $f(a) + bf'(a)$, so that b can be determined from a linear equation to give an approximation to a root $a + b$ of $f(x) = 0$. This method is applicable to non-algebraic equations.

78.17. Calculate a positive root of $x = \tan x$ to five decimal places.

79.1. The determinant formed from the derivatives $\partial f_i / \partial x_j$ is called the *Jacobian* of the n polynomials f in the n indeterminates x. A necessary and sufficient condition for the existence of a polynomial $F(f_1, \cdots, f_n)$, which does not vanish identically in $\Re[f_1, \cdots, f_n]$ but does vanish identically in $\Re[x_1, \cdots, x_n]$, is the vanishing of the Jacobian. Show how to construct F.

79.2. Extend the result of Exercise 79.1 to a system of m polynomials whose functional matrix is of rank r. (J. König, *Theorie der algebraischen Grössen*, Leipzig, 1903, p. 258.)

79.3. The elementary symmetric polynomials are functionally independent.

83.11. Any root of a polynomial with positive degree and rational coefficients is called an algebraic number. The totality of algebraic numbers forms a field.

83.12. The trigonometric functions of one degree and those of any rational multiple of one degree are algebraic numbers.

83.13. Apply Exercise 79.2 to find the formulas of Exercises 83.1 and 83.2.

83.14. If the commutative law is not assumed for the multiplication of indeterminates, what are the elementary symmetric polynomials in two indeterminates? Show by an example that Theorem 83.3 is not true. Show how its validity can be restored by augmenting the set E_1, E_2. (M. C. Wolf, Duke Mathematical Journal, vol. 2 (1936), p. 626.)

85.14. Prove Waring's formula.

85.15. If s_k is the Σ-polynomial of positive index k for the derivative f' and if all n (> 1) roots of f are non-negative, then $(n - 1)s_k \geqq ns'_k$. (Popovici's theorem.)

95.5. Find the effect of the transformations of Sec. 65 on the resultant and discriminant.

95.6. The eliminant on p. 171 is a linear polynomial in f, g but x appears in its coefficients. Show how to find a polynomial $F(f, g)$ which belongs to $\Re[f, g]$, which is not identically zero in f, g but is identically zero in $\Re[x]$.

95.7. Apply the result of Exercise 95.6 to Exercise 79.2.

96.1. The expression $(x_1 - x_3)(x_2 - x_4)/(x_1 - x_4)(x_2 - x_3)$ assumes six distinct forms under the permutations of the symmetric group of degree 4. If the x's are roots of the quartic

$$a_0x^4 + 4a_1x^3 + 6a_2x^2 + 4a_3x + a_4,$$

show that the polynomial (cross-ratio sextic) having the six fractions for roots is

$$g_2^3(x + 1)^2(x - 2)^2(x - \tfrac{1}{2})^2 = 27g_3^2(x + \omega)^3(x + \omega^2)^3,$$

where

$$g_2 = a_0a_4 - 4a_1a_3 + 3a_2^2,$$
$$g_3 = a_0a_2a_4 + 2a_1a_2a_3 - a_0a_3^2 - a_1^2a_4 - a_2^3.$$

96.2. Find the reduced form of the resolvent cubic of Exercise 71.6 in terms of g_2, g_3.

BIBLIOGRAPHY

BURNSIDE, W. S., and A. W. PANTON: *Theory of Equations*, London, 1928.

CAJORI, F.: *Introduction to the Modern Theory of Equations*, New York, 1904.

DICKSON, L. E.: *Elementary Theory of Equations*, New York, 1914.

——: *First Course in the Theory of Equations*, New York, 1922.

KLEIN, F.: *Famous Problems of Elementary Geometry*, translated by W. W. Beman and D. E. Smith, 2d edition, revised and enlarged with notes by R. C. Archibald, New York, 1930.

KOWALEWSKI, G.: *Einführung in die Determinantentheorie*, Leipzig, 1909.

MATHEWS, G. B.: *Algebraic Equations*, Cambridge, 1930.

PETERSEN, J.: *Theorie der algebraischen Gleichungen*, Copenhagen, 1878.

WEBER, H.: *Lehrbuch der Algebra*, vols. 1–2, Braunschweig, 1899–1912.

WEISNER, L.: *Introduction to the Theory of Equations*, New York, 1938.

INDEX

A

Absolute value, 6, 72
Additive function, 122
Albert, A. A., 40
Algebraic complement, 29, 30
Algebraic system, 183
Algorithm, division, 5, 62
Alternating group, 24
Alternating polynomial, 182
Amplitude, 70, 72
Approximation, 2, 130, 132
Arbitrary unknown, 46
Archibald, R. C., vi, 168, 197
Argand diagram, 72, 88
Arrangement, 15
Associated polynomial, 66
Associative, 1
Augmented matrix, 49, 50
Axiom of continuity, 3, 119

B

Becker, G. F., 111
Beman, W. W., 197
Birkhoff, G. D., 194
Blichfeldt, H. F., 24
Blumenthal, L. M., 193
Bôcher, M., 40, 53, 193
Bordered determinant, 37
Brand, L., 193
Budan's theorem, v, 125
Burgess, H. T., 53
Burnside, W. S., 197

C

Cahen, E., 195
Cajori, F., 197
Cardan, H., 107
Carlitz, L., vi
Closed, 1
Coefficient, 54
Column, 25
Commutative, 2, 18
Complement, algebraic, 29
Complete residue system, 12
Complex, 3, 72
Complex number, cartesian form, 72
Composite, 4
Congruence, 11
Conjugate, under symmetric group, 141
Conjugate complex, 72, 142
Conjugate constructible numbers, 159, 163
Conjugate imaginary, 98, 108
Constant, 54
Constructibility, 154
Constructible number, 158
    conjugate, 159, 163
    imaginary, 159
Constructible regular polygons, 165
Continuity, axiom of, 3, 119
Coordinates, cartesian, 69
    polar, 70
    rectangular. 69

199

Cramer's rule, 42
Cube, duplication of, 164
Cube roots of unity, 84
Cubic, 105
  irreducible case, 109, 112, 116
  real, 107
  reduced, 105
  resolvent, 115
Curves, derived, 71
Cycle, 16
Cyclotomic equation, 90

D

Degree, of group, 23, 24
  in indeterminate, 139
  of monomial, 54, 139
  of permutation, 24
  of polynomial, 54
De Moivre's theorem, 76
Depressed polynomial, 98
Depression, 81
Derivative, 59, 70
  roots of, 61, 121
  sign of, 70, 80
Derived curves, 71
Descartes' rule of signs, 125
Descartes' solution of quartic, 114
Determinant, 25
Diagonal, 25
Dialytic elimination, 171
Dickson, L. E., v, 14, 167, 197
Digit, 137
Diminishing roots, 102
Discriminant, 178
  of cubic, 108
  of n indeterminates, 181
  of quadratic, 104
Distributive, 2
Division of polynomials, 55
Division, synthetic, 56

Division algorithm, 5
  for polynomials, 62
Divisor, 4
Double root, 61
Duplication of the cube, 164

E

Eisenstein's theorem, 67
$e^{i\theta}$, 77
Elementary symmetric polynomials, 96
Elementary transformations, 27, 28, 33, 38
Eliminant, 172
Elimination, 8, 49, 172, 175
Equation, binomial, 91
  cubic, 105
  cyclotomic, 90
  higher degree, 117
  irreducible, 64
  quadratic, 103
  quartic, 114
  real cubic, 107
  reducible, 64
  solvable, 118
Euclid's algorithm, 5
Euler, L., 12, 116
Even integer, 5
Even permutation, 22
Expansion of determinant, 32, 33
Extension, 100
Extremum, 81

F

Factor theorem, 58
Factorization, 4, 22
  unique, 10
Famous problems, 154

Ferrari, L., 116
Ferro, S. del, 107
Field, 2
Fine, H. B., 14, 77, 93, 126
Frank, G., v
Franklin, P., 193
Fricke, R., 92
Frumveller, A. F., 194
Function, rational, 139
    symmetric, 142
Fundamental set, 52
Fundamental theorem of algebra, 93

G

Galois, E., v
Garver, R., 191
Gauss, C. F., 168
Gauss' lemma, 64
General solution, 9, 45
Graph, 70
Greeks, 154

H

Higher, 144
Highest common factor, 7, 61, 170, 173, 177
Horner's method, v, 132, 185
Hump, 81
Hurwitz, A., 81, 122
Hyperbolic functions, 110, 138

I

i, 1
Identically equal, 141
Identically zero, 140
Identity, 17
Imaginary, 3

Imaginary constructible number, 159
Imaginary roots, 98
    location and computation of, 188
Indeterminate, 41, 54, 160
Index, 143
Inequation, 183
Inflexion, 81
Initial, 54
Integer, 1
Interval, 74
Invariant, 27
Inverse, 19, 20
Irrational, 2
Irreducible, 64
Irreducible case of cubic, 109, 112

K

k-fold root, 61
Klein, F., 154, 168, 197
König, J., 195
Kowalewski, G., 40, 53, 192, 197
Kronecker, L., 66
Kronecker delta, 31

L

Lambert, W. D., 110
Laplace, P. S., 192
Leader, 26, 54
Least common multiple, 10, 21
Lehmer, E., 90
Like monomials, 140
Linear equation, approximation by, 130
Linear form, 49, 50, 51
Linear system, 41
Linearly dependent, 49
Location of roots, imaginary, 188
    real, 118

M

McGavock, W. G., vi
Main diagonal, 25, 30
Mathews, G. B., 197
Matrix, 25, 38, 48
Maximum, 81
Mertens, F., 178
Michel, C., 195
Minimum, 81
Minor, 29, 30
Modulo m, 11
Modulo 2π, 76
Modulus, of complex number, 72
  of congruence, 11
Monomial, 54
  in several indeterminates, 139
Morris, W. L., vi
Multilinear, 141, 161
Multiple roots, 61
Multiplicity of root, 61
Multiplying roots, 101

N

Netto, E., 24
Newton's formulas, 149
Non-homogeneous system, 49
Non-trivial solution, 47
Normal form, 158
Number, constructible, 158

O

Odd integer, 5
Odd permutation, 22
Odoms, A., vi
Order of radical, 158
Ordinal, 184
Orstrand, C. E. van, 111

P

Panton, A. W., 197
Parameter, 46
Parametric unknown, 185
Parity, 22
Period, of permutation, 16, 21
  of root of unity, 85, 88
Permutable, 18
Permutation, 15
  signed, 26
Petersen, J., 197
ϕ-function, 12
Polar form of complex number, 72
Polynomial, of algebraic system, 183
  alternating, 182
  associated, 66
  multilinear, 141
  in one indeterminate, 54
  in several indeterminates, 139
  Σ-, 143
  symmetric, 142
  unit, 64, 67
Polynomial ring, 55, 139
Popovici, M. T., 196
Powers, 19
Prime, 4
  relatively, 5
Primitive root of unity, 86
Product, of determinants, 32
  of permutations, 17
Proper root, 121
Pure imaginary, 3

Q

Quadratic, 103
Quadratic surd roots, 99
Quartic, 114

R

$\mathfrak{R}$, 2
Rank, of matrix, 38
  of set of linear forms, 49
Rational, 2
Rational roots, 96
Real, 2
Reducible, 63
Regular polygon, 165
Relatively prime, 5, 62
Remainder, 5, 55
Remainder theorem, 58
Residue, 12
Residue system, complete, 12
Resolvent cubic, 115
Resultant, 171, 175
Riccati, V., 110
Riesz, F., 193
Ring, 2
  polynomial, 55, 139
Ring operations, 178
Ritt, J. F., 54
Rolle's theorem, 121
Root, double, 61
  of equation, 59
  imaginary, 98, 108
  of inequation, 183
  k-fold, 61
  location of, 118, 188
  multiple, 61, 63
  of polynomial, 59
  primitive, 86
  proper, 121
  quadratic surd, 99
  rational, 96
  real, 104, 118, 129
  simple, 61, 63
  sums of powers of, 149
  triple, 61
  of unity, 83

Rotation of the plane, 76
Row, 25
Ruler and compass, 154

S

Schoenberg, I. J., 195
Schur, I., 90
Secondary diagonal, 25, 27
Segment, 74, 122
Separating number, 119
Sequence, 6
sgn, 120
Short, W. T., 110
Σ-polynomial, 143
Sign, variation of, 122
Signed permutation, 26
Simple root, 61
Simultaneous equations, 183
Slope, 43, 70
Smith, D. E., 197
Solution, general, 9, 45
  non-trivial, 47
  particular, 45
  trivial, 47
Solutions, fundamental set of, 52
Solvable, 118
Standard form, 140
Stokes, R. W., vi, 193
Straight line, 43
Sturm's sequence, 127
Sturm's theorem, v, 128
Summation convention, 30, 31
Sylvester's dialytic elimination, 171
Symmetric function, 142, 152
Symmetric group, 23
Symmetric polynomials, elementary, 96
Synthetic division, 56

System, algebraic, 183
  coordinate, 69
  homogeneous, 44
  linear, 41
  non-homogeneous, 49

T

Tangent, 70
Tartaglia, 107
Taylor development, 79
Totient, 12
Transformation, elementary, 27, 28, 33, 38
  of equations, 101
Transpose, 27, 49
Transposition, 16
Trigonometric solution of cubic in irreducible case, 109
Triple root, 61
Trisection of angle, 164
Trivial solution, 47

U

Unique factorization, 10
Unit, 4
Unit circle, 89
Unit length, 69, 155
Unit polynomial, 64, 67
Unity, roots of, 83

Unknown, 41
  parametric, 185

V

Value, absolute, 6, 72
Van Vleck, E. B., 194
Variation of sign, 122
Veblen, O., 31, 193

W

Wade, L. I., vi
Waerden, B. L. van der, 66, 68, 192
Waring's formula, 151, 195
Weber, H., 90, 92, 114, 197
Weight, 65, 143
Weisner, L., 197
Wellstein, J., 114
Wolf, M. C., 195

X

x, 2

Y

Young, J. W. A., 167

Z

$\mathfrak{z}$, 3
Zero, identically, 140

ANSWERS TO EXERCISES

3.1. 368, 272, 96, 80, 16, 0.

3.2. 71, −53, 18, 1, 0.

3.3. 407, 275, 132, 11, 0.

3.4. 180.

3.5. 11.

4.1. $2^2 \cdot 3^2$.

4.2. $2^2 \cdot 3 \cdot 5$.

4.3. $2^3 \cdot 3 \cdot 5$.

5.1. 3.

5.2. 4.

5.3. 3.

7.1. (1265)(34).

7.2. (147)(26)(35).

8.1. (12).

8.2. (23).

8.3. 1.

8.4. (164235).

8.5. (2643).

10.1. $S^2 = (13524)$, $S^3 = (14253)$, $S^4 = (15432)$, $S^5 = 1$. $S^{-1} = S^4$, $S^{-2} = S^3$, $S^{-3} = S^2$, $S^{-4} = S$, $S^{-5} = 1$. Period of $S^5 = 1$ is unity. That of the others is 5.

10.2. $T^2 = (354)$, $T^3 = (12)$, $T^4 = (345)$, $T^5 = (12)(354)$, $T^6 = 1$; $T^{-1} = T^5$, $T^{-2} = T^4$, $T^{-3} = T^3$, $T^{-4} = T^2$, $T^{-5} = T$. Period of $T^6 = 1$ is one, periods of T, T^2, T^3, T^4, T^5 are 6, 3, 2, 3, 6.

10.3. (12).

10.4. (132).

10.5. (12)(34).

10.6. (132)(465).

10.7. (452)(132).

12.1. $(12)^5(13)(23)(34)$.

14.2. $(-1)^{\frac{1}{2}n(n-1)}$.

22.1. 2.
22.2. 2.
22.3. 0.
22.4. -11.
22.5. 12.
22.6. 0.
22.7. $abc - af^2 - bg^2 - ch^2 + 2fgh$.
22.8. 1.
22.9. -380.
22.10. $(af - be + cd)^2$.

24.1. 2.
24.2. 2.
24.3. 3.
24.4. 2.
24.5. 2.
24.6. 3.
24.7. 4, or less if the letters have special values.

25.1. $(3, 2)$.
25.2. $(3, 2, 1)$.
25.3. $x = \dfrac{(c - d)(d - b)}{(c - a)(a - b)}$.
25.4. $(1, -1, 2, -2)$.

27.1. $5x = 23z - 28t$, $5y = 22z - 27t$.
27.2. $x = -2z - t - u$, $y = -z - t - \frac{4}{3}u$.
27.3. $x = -55t$, $y = 62t$, $z = 71t$.
27.4. $38x = -19z - 43t - 45u$, $19y = 19z + 32t + 22u$.
27.5. $x = z + 2t$, $y = -z - t$.
27.6. $(0, 0, 0)$.

28.1. $5x = 23z + 28$, $5y = 22z + 27$.
28.2. $x = -2z - t + 1$, $y = -z - t + \frac{4}{3}$.
28.3. $(55, -62, -71)$.
28.4. $38x = -19z - 43t + 45$, $38y = 38z + 64t - 44$.
28.5. $x = z - 2$, $y = -z + 1$.
28.6. Inconsistent.

31.1. $\frac{1}{8}(4x^2 - 2x + 13)$, $-\frac{5}{8}$.
31.2. $\frac{1}{9}(9x^2 - 6x + 13)$, $\frac{1}{9}(-59x + 31)$.
31.3. $2x^2 - 3x + 2$, 0.

31.4. $3x^3 + 5x^2 - 4x + 2, 0.$
31.5. $3x^2 + 4x - 2, 0.$
31.6. $\frac{1}{4}(6x + 11), \frac{1}{4}(x - 7).$

33.1. $2x + 1, 2, 0.$
33.2. $10x^4 + 12x^2 - 5, 40x^3 + 24x, 120x^2 + 24, 240x, 240, 0.$
33.3. $5(x - 1)^4, 20(x - 1)^3, 60(x - 1)^2, 120(x - 1), 120, 0.$

35.1. $x - 1.$
35.2. $x^2 - x - 2.$
35.3. $1.$
35.4. $2x + 1.$
35.5. $x^3 + 2x + 1.$

36.1. $1.$
36.2. $2.$
36.3. $-2.$
36.4. $x^3 + 2x^2 + 2x + 1.$
36.5. $x^3 + x^2 + 4.$
36.6. $x^2 - x + 1.$

44.1. $-1.$
44.2. $1.$
44.3. $1.$
44.4. $i.$
44.5. $\sin 3\theta = 3 \sin \theta - 4 \sin^3 \theta, \cos 3\theta = 4 \cos^3 \theta - 3 \cos \theta.$

45.1. $\delta = .01.$
45.2. $\delta = .0004.$
45.3. $\delta = .003.$

48.1. $e^{\frac{1}{2}\pi i} = i, e^{\pi i} = -1, e^{\frac{3}{2}\pi i} = -i, 1.$
48.2. $e^{\frac{1}{3}\pi i} = \frac{1}{2} + \frac{1}{2}\sqrt{3}i, -\frac{1}{2} + \frac{1}{2}\sqrt{3}i, -1, -\frac{1}{2} - \frac{1}{2}\sqrt{3}i, \frac{1}{2} - \frac{1}{2}\sqrt{3}i, 1.$
49.1. $-\frac{1}{2} \pm \frac{1}{2}\sqrt{3}i.$
49.2. $\pm i.$

52.1. $-\omega, \omega^2, -1, \omega, -\omega^2, 1.$

56.1. $x^4 + 1.$
56.2. $x^6 + x^3 + 1.$
56.3. $x^4 + x^3 + x^2 + x + 1.$
56.4. $x^4 - x^2 + 1.$
56.5. $x^8 - x^7 + x^5 - x^4 + x^3 - x + 1.$

61.1. $x^2 - 3x + 2$.
61.2. $x^3 - 6x^2 + 11x - 6$.
61.3. $x^4 - 10x^3 + 35x^2 - 50x + 24$.
61.4. $x^4 + 2x^3 - 13x^2 - 14x + 24$.
61.5. $2x^3 - x^2 - 2x + 1$.
61.6. $x^3 - 3x^2 + 4x - 2$.
61.7. $12x^4 - 20x^3 - 5x^2 + 10x + 3$.
61.8. $x^4 - 6x^3 + 13x^2 - 12x + 4$.
61.9. $\frac{3}{2}$, 2.
61.10. 0, -1, -5.
61.11. 0, $-\frac{2}{3}$, $-\frac{4}{3}$, $-\frac{1}{3}$.
61.12. 0, 0, 0, -1.

62.1. $-\frac{1}{2}$.
62.2. $-\frac{1}{3}$, $\frac{1}{2}$.
62.3. -1, $\frac{2}{3}$.
62.4. None.
62.5. $-\frac{2}{3}$, $\frac{1}{4}$, $\frac{1}{2}$, $\frac{3}{2}$.

63.1. $x^4 - 2x^3 + 3x^2 - 2x + 2$.

65.1. $y^3 + 3y^2 + 6y + 4$.
65.2. $y^4 - 7y^3 + 36y^2 - 216$.
65.3. $y^4 + 19y^3 - 144y^2 - 1872y + 10368$.
65.4. $y^3 - 9y + 9$.
65.5. $y^4 - 76y^3 - 576y^2 + 71424y - 663552$.
65.6. $4y^3 - 5y + 4$.
65.7. $27y^4 - 36y^2 - 34y - 3$.

67.1. -1, $3\omega - 1$, $3\omega^2 - 1$.
67.2. 8, $-\omega$, $-\omega^2$.
67.3. $1 + 2^{\frac{1}{3}} + 2^{\frac{2}{3}}$, $1 + 2^{\frac{1}{3}}\omega + 2^{\frac{2}{3}}\omega^2$, $1 + 2^{\frac{1}{3}}\omega^2 + 2^{\frac{2}{3}}\omega$.
67.4. $-\frac{3}{2}$, $\frac{3}{2}\omega$, $\frac{3}{2}\omega^2$.
67.5. -5, -5, 1.
67.6. $(a + b + c)(a + b\omega + c\omega^2)(a + b\omega^2 + c\omega)$.

68.1. 756.
68.2. 216.
68.3. 3024.
68.4. -176.
68.5. 0.

69.1. -4.602, -1.660, 0.262.
69.2. -1.449, 3.449, 4.000(exact).
69.3. -3.942, -1.442, -0.616.

71.1. -5, -2, 1, 2.

71.2. $-\frac{3}{2}$, $\frac{1}{2}$, $-\frac{1}{2} + 2\omega$, $-\frac{1}{2} + 2\omega^2$.

71.3. $\pm i$, $2 \pm 2i$.

71.4. $1 \pm \frac{1}{2}\sqrt{2}$, $-3 \pm \frac{1}{2}\sqrt{2}i$.

71.5. $\frac{3}{2} \pm \frac{1}{2}\sqrt{15}$, $\frac{1}{2} \pm \frac{1}{2}\sqrt{5}i$.

71.7. $-\frac{3}{2} \pm \frac{1}{2}\sqrt{5}$, $-\frac{1}{2} \pm \frac{1}{2}\sqrt{11}i$.

71.8. $ad^2 = b^2e$, $64a^3e = (b^2 - 4ac)^2$.

71.9. $b^4 = 256a^3e$, $c^2 = 36ae$, $d^4 = 256ae^3$.

76.1. $x^2 + 4x + 2$, $2x + 3$, 1. $[-5, -4; -2, -1; 0, 1]$.

76.2. $x^2 - 4x + 1$, $3x - 11$, 1. $[-2, -1; 3, 3\frac{1}{2}; 3\frac{1}{2}, 4]$.

76.3. $x^2 + 4x + 3$, $4x + 5$, 1. $[-4, -3; -2, -1; -1, 0]$.

76.4. $3x^2 - 6x - 1$, $2x + 1$, -1. $[3, 4]$.

76.5. $g_0 = f/(2x - 1) = 2x^2 + 7x - 4$, $g_1 = 4x + 7$, $g_2 = 1$. $[-5, -4; 0, 1]$.

76.6. $3x^2 + x + 1$, $-11x + 10$, -1. $[0, 1]$.

76.7. $x^3 - x^2 + x + 1$, $-x^2 - 5x - 2$, $-29x - 13$, 1.   No real roots.

76.8. $2x^3 - x + 1$, $x^2 - 3x + 2$, $-13x + 11$, -1. $[-2, -1; 0, 1]$.

76.9. $7x^3 + 21x^2 + 17x + 3$, $2x^2 + 4x + 1$, $x + 1$, 1. $[-2, -\frac{3}{2}; -\frac{3}{2}, -1; -\frac{1}{2}, -\frac{1}{4}; -\frac{1}{4}, 0]$.

76.10. $56x^3 - 84x^2 + 34x - 3$, $8x^2 - 8x + 1$, $2x - 1$, 1. $[0, \frac{1}{8}; \frac{1}{8}, \frac{3}{4}; \frac{3}{4}, \frac{7}{8}; \frac{7}{8}, 1]$.

78.1. $\pm 1.414\ 21$.

78.2. $.434\ 258$, $-.767\ 591$.

78.3. $2.080\ 08$.

78.4. $1.165\ 90$.

78.5. $2.843\ 73$.

78.6. $-1.074\ 34$.

78.7. $-3.601\ 67$, $-0.660\ 123$, $1.261\ 80$.

78.8. $-2.667\ 83$, $1.667\ 83$.

78.9. $-3.024\ 42$, $-0.914\ 050$, $0.877\ 626$, $2.060\ 85$.

78.10. $0.099\ 999$.

83.1. $E_1^2 - 2E_2$.

83.2. $E_2^2 - 2E_1E_3 + 2E_4$.

83.3. $E_1^3 - 3E_1E_2 + 3E_3$.

83.4. $E_2E_3 - 3E_1E_4 + 5E_5$.

83.5. $E_3^2 + 2E_1E_5 - 2E_2E_4 - 2E_6$.

83.6. $E_1E_2^2 - 2E_1^2E_3 + 5E_1E_4 - E_2E_3 - 5E_5$.

83.7. $E_1E_2E_3 - 3E_1^2E_4 + 7E_1E_5 + 4E_2E_4 - 3E_3^2 - 12E_6$.

83.8. $E_1^4 - 4E_1^2E_2 + 4E_1E_3 + 2E_2^2 - 4E_4$.

83.9. $E_1^3E_2 - E_1^2E_3 - 3E_1E_2^2 + E_1E_4 + 5E_2E_3 - 5E_5$.

83.10. $E_1^2E_2^2 - 2E_1^3E_3 + 2E_1^2E_4 + 4E_1E_2E_3 - 6E_1E_5 - 2E_2^3 + 2E_2E_4$
$- 3E_3^2 + 6E_6$.

85.1. $E_1^2 - 2E_2$.

85.2. $E_1^3 - 3E_1E_2 + 3E_3$.

85.3. $E_1^4 - 4E_1^2E_2 + 4E_1E_3 + 2E_2^2 - 4E_4$.

85.4. $E_1^5 - 5E_1^3E_2 + 5E_1^2E_3 + 5E_1E_2^2 - 5E_1E_4 - 5E_2E_3 + 5E_5$.

85.5. $E_1^6 - 6E_1^4E_2 + 6E_1^3E_3 + 9E_1^2E_2^2 - 6E_1^2E_4 - 12E_1E_2E_3 + 6E_1E_5$
$- 2E_2^3 + 6E_2E_4 + 3E_3^2 - 6E_6$.

85.6. -2076.

85.7. 4095.

85.8. -124.

85.9. $-\frac{191}{4}$.

85.10. $\frac{1}{6}(s_1^3 - 3s_1s_2 + 2s_3)$.

85.11. $s_1s_2 - s_3$.

85.12. $\frac{1}{2}(s_2^2 - s_4)$.

85.13. $\frac{1}{2}(s_1^2s_2 - 2s_1s_3 - s_2^2 + 2s_4)$.

86.1. $E_{n-1}E_n^{-1}$.

86.2. $E_1E_{n-1}E_n^{-1} - n$.

88.1. $x^4 - 8x^2 + 12 = 0$.

88.3. $x^8 - 16x^6 + 68x^4 - 128x^2 + 4 = 0$.

92.1. $x^2 + x - 6;\ 2,\ -3$.

92.2. $x^2 + x + 1;\ \omega,\ \omega^2$.

92.3. $x - 1;\ 1$.

92.4. $x^2 + x - 2;\ 1,\ -2$.

92.5. None.

93.1. $(ab' - a'b)(bc' - b'c) - (ac' - a'c)^2$.

93.2. $(ab' - a'b)x + ac' - a'c$.

95.2. $D_3 = D_4$.

95.3. $(-1)^{\frac{1}{2}(n-1)(n-2)}n^n$.

95.4. $18abcd - 27a^2d^2 + b^2c^2 - 4ac^3 - 4b^3d$.

98.1. $2x^4 - 9x^2 + 4x + 3,\ xy + 2x^2 - 1$.

98.2. $x^5 + x^4 - 8x^3 + 9x^2 - 22x + 24,\ (x^2 - 3)y + 2x - 5$.

98.3. $x^2 + 4x - 12,\ y^2 - 2y - 8;\ (2, 4),\ (2, -2),\ (-6, 4),\ (-6, -2)$

98.4. $x(x - 4)(x^2 - 4x + 3),\ (x - 2)y + x - 4;\ (0, -2),\ (1, -3)$
$(3, 1),\ (4, 0)$.

98.5. $2x^4 - x^2 + 1$, $xy + x^2 - 1$.

98.6. $x + 1 \neq 0$, $y + 1 = 0$, $(x + 1)z + x - 3 = 0$.

98.7. $x^2 - 1$, $y + x$, $xz - 2$; $(1, -1, 2)$, $(-1, 1, -2)$.

98.8. $x = 0$, $y \neq 0$, $z = 0$; $x = 0$, $y = 0$; $x \neq 0$, $y = 0$, $z - 2x = 0$; $x \neq 0$, $y - x = 0$, $z + x = 0$.

98.9. $x = 0$, $y^2 + y = 0$; $x \neq 0$, $y + x = 0$.

98.10. $x = 0$, $y = 0$, $z = 0$; $x \neq 0$, $y^2 - xy = 0$, $(x + y)z + 4xy - 2x^2$.

99.3. 1, $-\frac{1}{2} \pm \frac{1}{2}\sqrt{3}i$.

99.4. $-\frac{3}{2}$, $-\frac{1}{2} \pm \frac{1}{2}\sqrt{3}i$.

99.5. $\frac{1}{2}$, $2 \pm 3i$.

99.6. $-i$, $i \pm 1$.

99.7. $i \pm 1$, $i + 2$.